FOUNDATIONS OF

Related Fitness

IN PHYSICAL EDUCATION

The Ling Publishing House
162 Kings Cross Road, London WC1X 9DH

Published by
Ling Publishing House
162 Kings Cross Road
London WC1X 9DH

ISBN 0 900985 17 8

Photo acknowledgements:
**North Staffordshire Polytechnic Educational
Development Unit (media services)
Ken Fox
Jim Whitehead
and members of the Physical Education Association
of G.B. and N.I.**

Typeset by
New Faces – Bedford

Produced by
Concept Design Associates

Printed in Great Britain by
**Graphic Litho Ltd
Woodfield Road
Welwyn Garden City**

Contents

Editor – Stuart J. H. Biddle

Contributors

Mr. Neil Armstrong
Neil Armstrong is an exercise physiologist lecturing at Exeter University and has published extensively in physiology and HRF, primarily in paediatric physiology.

Mr. Stuart Biddle
Stuart Biddle specialises in the psychology of exercise and sport, and HRF. He has published extensively in these areas. He is a lecturer at North Staffordshire Polytechnic, Stoke-on-Trent.

Mr. Steve Cook
Steve Cook is a deputy head teacher at Bilton Grange High School in Kingston-upon-Hull and has a particular interest in the role of physical and health education in pupils' personal and social development.

Dr. Charles Corbin
Dr. Corbin is a Professor of Health and Physical Education at Arizona State University where he specialises in HRF and the psychology of exercise and sport. He is a world leader in HRF and has published several books, including (with Dr. Ruth Lindsey) 'Fitness for Life' and 'Concepts of Physical Fitness', as well as over 100 professional and research papers.

Ms. Fiona Dowling
Fiona Dowling taught physical education in schools before becoming the Project Officer for the PEA/HEC Health and Physical Education Project, based at Loughborough University.

Mr. Ken Fox
Ken Fox lectures in HRF at Northern Illinois University, USA. He previously studied with Dr. Charles Corbin at both Kansas State and Arizona State Universities. He has published extensively in HRF and has been a leading innovator of HRF in Britain having worked at Rawlins Community College, Leicestershire.

Mr. Alan Hargreaves
Alan Hargreaves was formerly head of the Madeley School of Physical Education, North Staffordshire Polytechnic, where he specialised in curriculum work. He has wide experience in the teaching of games and fitness.

Mr. Tom Mercer
Tom Mercer is a lecturer at North Staffordshire Polytechnic where he specialises in exercise physiology, sports medicine and team games. He has a Masters degree in Coaching Science from Canada.

Mr. Stephen Pain
Steve Pain is the Education Officer for Schools at the Health Education Council. He is a former teacher of physical education and was instrumental in the setting-up of the PEA/HEC Health and Physical Education Project.

Dr. Robert Pangrazi
Dr. Pangrazi is Professor/Chair in the Department of Health and Physical Education, Arizona State University. He is a world leader in physical education for primary children having published extensively in the field, including being co-author of 'Dynamic Physical Education for Elementary School Children'.

Mr. Andrew Sparkes
Andy Sparkes is a lecturer in the Department of Physical Education and Sports Science, Loughborough University. He is currently completing his Ph.D. in curriculum change and has published papers on the role of competition in physical education.

Mr. Jim Whitehead
Jim Whitehead is currently on the Ph.D. programme in physical education at Arizona State University under the supervision of Dr. Charles Corbin. Previously, he taught at Rawlins Community College, Leicestershire, where he became a leading innovator of HRF in Britain.

Introduction

Physical educationists are often in a 'catch 22' situation when it comes to curriculum innovation or change. If they don't change they confirm the conservative stereotype, while if they do implement change they are seen to be leaping on the next available, yet apparently transient, 'bandwagon'. Without debating the merits or otherwise of previous attempts to introduce significant changes in physical education, one shift of focus has had such a major impact in the 1980's that many teachers are questioning their philosophy across the whole programme, rather than just in one or two specific units of work. This shift is in 'health-related fitness'. Whilst we may not all agree on the term itself, health-related fitness (HRF) shares a common 'fitness for life' philosphy congruent with the egalitarian aims of education for a lifetime. It not only reflects the need to encourage more active lifestyles in a sedentary society, it also provides a physical education medium through which all people can enjoy 'success' at their own level, can see improvement, and can participate without the necessary comparisons of competition.

HRF activities are truly lifelong, hence providing pupils with life skills in the hope that we can achieve higher participation rates in physical activity for adults. Such issues are the content of this book. Teachers are keen to improve on any pre-service deficiencies in this area of their work, and this book has been compiled in an effort to provide the necessary foundations.

The book is primarily the result of the initiatives of Ken Fox and Andrew Petherick. At the 1985 ICHPER conference, Ken Fox suggested that the 1985/86 *British Journal of Physical Education* series on HRF, by Corbin, Fox and Whitehead, be put into a book alongside other key chapters. This final version has expanded from these original ideas as an extra 12 chapters have been added to the Corbin series. The book is not intended as a day-to-day practical teaching manual, but rather as providing foundation material in HRF necessary for effective teaching.

Section A provides a philosophy and rationale, based around the initial Corbin et al paper 'Fitness for a lifetime'. This is suitably followed by Fiona Dowling's chapter on a health focus in physical education and the rationale behind the PEA/HEC Health and Physical Education project, on which she is currently Project Officer. Neil Armstrong's physiological rationale provides sound scientific grounds for implementation of such work and this chapter has been well received in lectures throughout Britain.

Section B provides a basic knowledge base in each of the main components of HRF centred around the Corbin et al series. Chapters have been added on nutrition and stress management.

Section C focuses more specifically on the teaching of HRF with the Fox et al chapter on 'Getting started' providing much-needed advice on the initial steps for successful curriculum innovation. Chapter 11, in fact, provides more detail on the nature of one such innovation actually implemented in Britain by Fox and Whitehead. Robert Pangrazi provides a chapter on HRF for primary-age children with a series of activities suitable for stimulating interest at this level. This is clearly an area where further developments are needed. Finally, an example teaching-learning unit is provided by Alan Hargreaves with an 8-week programme on cardiovascular fitness. This is a practical chapter based on sound curriculum principles.

Section D considers other important HRF issues which often provide much debate at in-service courses and conferences. Steve Cook's chapter looks at the practical issues of how we can learn from health education, while chapters are also included on the potentially difficult areas of motivation and the place of competition. Fitness testing always stimulates much debate and the Biddle and Fox chapter outlines a cautious yet practical approach to the subject. Neil Armstrong continues the debate with a scientific appraisal of test validity.

It is hoped that this book will be a landmark publication in the expanding area of HRF. I am indebted to Dr. Charles B. Corbin, Ken Fox and Jim Whitehead for their leadership in HRF. They have been an inspiration to me and, through this book and other publications, to many more people. My thanks go to Andrew Petherick, General Secretary of the PEA, and all of the authors, who helped produce this book.

Good luck in promoting lifetime fitness.

Stuart Biddle

Section A

Philosophy and Rationale

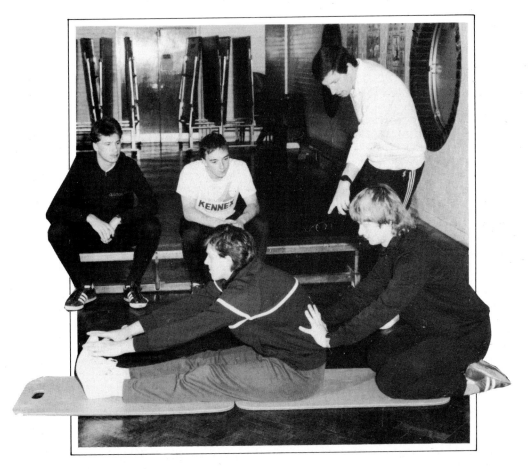

Chapter One

Fitness for a Lifetime

Charles Corbin, Ken Fox &
Jim Whitehead

One of the major innovations in physical education programmes in recent years has been the emergence of interest in the teaching of health-related fitness. This drive towards the inclusion of fitness in the curriculum is primarily for the sake of improvement of the health and quality of life of students, and has not only occurred in Britain, but is already well-established in Australia, Canada and the United States. In these countries, text books and materials are readily available and health-related fitness is an important part of the programmes of many schools and colleges. During the past three years, a number of articles have attempted to give a rationale for the inclusion of health-related fitness teaching in the physical education programme. For those interested in further reading, this literature and other helpful material is presented at the end of this chapter. To date, there has been a lack of useful information and practical direction regarding the real mechanics of health-related fitness teaching. The logic behind the inclusion of health-related fitness in the curriculum is becoming widely accepted. Teachers wish to make the appropriate changes, but call for practical suggestions. This chapter, and related ones in this book, are designed to inform, update, and give help that may make the difficult task of innovation a little easier.

Skill-related versus health-related fitness

Our programmes have traditionally focused on helping children learn how to move well. This is particularly the case in early physical education, and secondary programmes attempt to refine these movement skills within the context of traditional sports and games, and other organized activities. These gross motor skills have been termed the *skill-related aspects of fitness,* and include abilities such as coordination, balance, agility, speed, reaction time, and power. Fortunately, they are abilities which improve with practice, and tend to stay

Figure 1: MUSCULAR ENDURANCE

with us once learnt. Sadly, they are also highly dependent on genetic factors, so that we all learn at different rates and have limited potential, few of us reaching excellence, but most of us at least achieving competence. The development of skill-related fitness has always, and will always be, a vital part of the curriculum. It is important in developing physical confidence, and helps us enjoy and perform well at dance, sports, recreational activities, and those aspects of work and everyday life which involve moving well.

Of equal importance in the curriculum are those aspects of fitness which are specially related to health and well-being. These components of *health-related fitness* include cardiovascular or aerobic fitness, strength and muscular endurance, flexibility, and desirable body composition (see figures 1, 2, 4, 5). Ideal levels of these aspects of fitness result from regular physical activity and exercise of the right type. Sports may promote some aspects of health-related fitness, but equally effective are activities such as jogging, swimming, aerobic dance, weight training, or simple exercises done at home. Unlike skill-related fitness which has a high retention, health-related fitness cannot be stored, and needs constant maintenance through regular activity. However, it is readily available to all students regardless of skill level, and the potential benefits are great. Its possession results in looking good and feeling well, having a high capacity to do physical work, and helps protect against the problems and disease associated with our 'take-it-easy' western culture. The facts about the benefits of regular exercise have already been well documented (Armstrong, chapter 3, Bassey & Fentem, 1981).

Figure 2: CARDIOVASCULAR ENDURANCE (aerobic fitness)

Teaching Lifetime Fitness
For the sake of discussion, it will be assumed

here that a programme of lifetime health-related physical fitness is important and worthy of consideration in schools. At first glance the development of such a programme seems to be a relatively easy task. Some would have us simply plan a programme containing a variety of vigorous physical activities including those designed to develop the five principle components of health-related fitness. If lifetime fitness is our goal, the job may not be as simple as it appears. We propose a stairway to lifetime fitness which includes objectives more comprehensive than merely exercising children and building their health-related fitness (see figure 3).

```
                              ⌐ ̄ ̄ ̄ ̄ ̄ ̄ ̄
                           ⌐__⌐ Problem Solving
                        ⌐__⌐ Evaluating
                     ⌐__⌐ Regular Exercise Patterns __ __ __ __
                  ⌐ __ ⌐ Achieving Fitness
               _ ⌐ Exercising
```

Figure 3: The Stairway to Health Related Fitness

Too often, those who want to build fitness, especially among our children, take the first two steps up the stairway and then stop. They believe that the goal of fitness in schools is to "get people to exercise". It is! But that is not all that needs to be done. It is easy enough to get young children to exercise; they often love it! It is often easy to take the second step, "to get youngsters fit". What may not be so easy is persuading people to maintain their exercise and fitness levels when the choice is theirs. A recent study in the United States (Ross & Gilbert, 1984), shows that although many more people report that they now involve regular exercise in their lifestyles, few do enough to maintain adequate levels of fitness. Also, the trend towards fitness does not appear to be a characteristic of large groups in the population such as blue-collar workers, and schoolchildren.

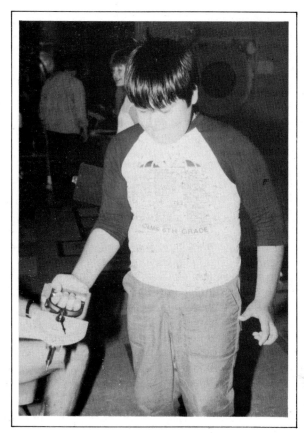

Figure 4: STRENGTH TESTING

There is evidence to suggest that the same two steps up the stairway to fitness while in school *may not be enough to keep you fit for a lifetime.*

Health-related fitness is a state of being. It is transient. If fitness is something we "do to" people, rather than something that people incorporate into their lifestyles because they think it is important, and enjoyable, it will not be maintained for a lifetime. The military services have provided good examples of this. Their trainees, through physical training programmes, take the first two steps up the stairway to fitness. However, in doing so they often learn to hate physical training. The fit soldier who has been trained to a fine state of health-related fitness, but who hates exercise is not likely to continue to climb the stairway to a lifetime of fitness. In the same way, children in schools may stop climbing if fitness is not made enjoyable and the benefits made clear.

After step two (as indicated by the dotted line) people need to begin to develop exercise patterns. Unlike steps one and two where someone else is in control, such as a teacher or drill instructor, step three is the beginning of personalised exercise. It is at this point that we help people to choose forms of exercise which suit their individual needs and interests. Instead of telling them what to do, we help them begin to make their own decisions. Once this step has been taken the fourth step is to help people to evaluate their own fitness. People who exercise and stay fit for a lifetime must be able to assess their own fitness. It is difficult to accurately plan a lifetime of activity without first knowing how to assess personal fitness and exercise needs. Our job in physical education, is not so much to evaluate our students (again doing something for them), but to help them learn to test themselves. People who have learnt how to select activities which meet their own needs and interests (step 4) and who know how to assess their own fitness levels (step 5) are able to take the sixth and final step on the stairway to fitness; they can now *learn to solve their own fitness problems.* Problem solving or independence from the teacher is the highest goal. When people reach this level they are no longer reliant on others. They know how to get fit and can plan their own personal programmes. They exercise because they value fitness, not because they are told to.

If we want all our students to reach the top of the stairway, we must give them the right kind of help and support. In a way, it is like holding their hand until they have taken a few steps. We must prevent them from falling back down to the bottom of the stairs as a result of failure and bad exercise experiences. As students gain in confidence with good experiences, we no longer need to hold their hands. They have learnt to climb on their own. Of course it is essential also, that students be

Figure 5: FLEXIBILITY

convinced that the top of the stairway is worth reaching. We need to help students see the benefits of regular exercise in the hope that they will feel that their efforts are worthwhile. The ultimate goal is to create a lasting desire in students, through their school experiences in physical activity, so that they choose to be involved for the rest of their lives.

It is clear then, that the teaching of health-related fitness is not without its problems. It is as important to develop healthy attitudes as well as healthy bodies. Those programmes which lean heavily towards competitive team sports will have to make radical changes if they wish to have a positive lasting effect on all students. Other programmes might only require subtle changes in emphasis or teaching style. Instructors will need to become familiar with the application of simple exercise physiology, and perhaps the principles of good nutrition and stress management. A working knowledge of how exercise and regular activity can affect our lives, and an understanding of the psychology of motivation for physical activity, will also help teachers to create an environment that encourages student involvement.

Because many of us completed our teacher preparation when the focus was more on skill-related rather than health-related physical fitness, we may need to brush up on the facts (many of the more relevant courses now offered in some teacher preparation institutions were not available when most of us went through teacher training). There has been a tremendous explosion in knowledge in the exercise sciences in recent years. A good summary of this information, and examples of its practical application, would prove useful to the teacher interested in teaching health-related fitness principles in the physical education curriculum.

It should also be noted that the developmental differences of students should be of particular concern in teaching for lifetime fitness. The developmental needs and interests vary with each age group. To be effective in developing sound attitudes, knowledge about fitness, and behaviour patterns which will be carried out for a lifetime, these differences must not be overlooked.

The goal of this chapter is to encourage readers to take on the challenge of change, and to incorporate a fitness for life philosophy into their physical education teaching. We believe it is a relevant and necessary part of the curriculum for ALL students.

References
ALMOND, L. (1983). Health-related fitness. *British Journal of Physical Education,* Vol. 14 (2).
BASSEY, E. J., & FENTEM, P. H. (1981). *Exercise: the facts,* Oxford: Oxford University Press.

BIDDLE, S. (1984). Motivational issues in health-related fitness: a note of caution. *British Journal of Physical Education,* Vol. 15 (1).

BULLETIN OF PHYSICAL EDUCATION (1983). *Health-related fitness in schools.* Vol. 19 (2).

CORBIN, C. B. (Sept. 1984). Fitness for life: a status report. *Physical Education Newsletter,* Vol. 162.

CORBIN, C. B. & LAURIE, D. R. (1978). Exercise for a lifetime: an educational effort. *The Physician and Sportsmedicine,* Vol. 6.

CORBIN, C. B. LINDSAY, R. (1985). *Concepts of Physical Fitness,* (Fifth Edition), Dubuque, Iowa: Wm. Brown Co., (formerly *Concepts in Physical Education.*

CORBIN, C. B., LINDSEY, R. & CARRE, A. (1982). *Fitness for life,* London: Gage Publ.

FITNESS CANADA, (1983). *Canadian fitness survey highlights.* Ottawa. Ontario: Government of Canada, 1983.

FOX, K. R. (1982). One Englishman's view of American P.E. and sport. *British Journal of Physical Education,* Vol. 13 (1).

FOX, K. R. (1983). Physical life skills: further thoughts on health-related fitness. *British Journal of Physical Education.* Vol. 14 (3).

FOX, K. R. (1983). Teaching physical life skills: practical ideas on health-related fitness. *British Journal of Physical Education* Vol. 14 (5).

HAWKINS, K. (1984). Physical education and sports: the gospel according to Australia. *British Journal of Physical Education,* Vol. 15 (5).

ROSS, J. G. & GILLBERT, G. G. (1984). *National Children and Youth Fitness Study,* Washington D.C. Office of Disease Prevention & Health Promotion.

WILLIAMS, P. (1984). Health-related fitness: an Australian perspective. *British Journal of Physical Education,* Vol. 15 (1).

This chapter first appeared in the *British Journal of Physical Education,* 1985, Vol 16 (2), 44-46.

Chapter Two

A Health Focus within Physical Education

Fiona Dowling

Health education in its broadest sense has changed dramatically in character over the past few decades. With the advances in medical science the incidence of many diseases has been substantially reduced, and as McCafferty (1979) points out "... the whole order of priorities for the prevention and cure of disease has in the course of sixty years changed almost completely". Health education now encompasses the positive facets of 'health' rather than merely concerning itself with curability. Indeed, the World Health Organisation defines health as being the 'state of complete physical, mental and social well being, not merely freedom from disease and infirmity'. A report by the Department of Health and Social Security (DHSS) in 1976 stated "The health problems facing us today ... are concerned with individual human behaviour or lifestyle rather than with massive problems of environmental health and infectious disease".

To this end, health education today is addressing healthful life practices. The Department of Education and Science (DES; 1981) in 'The School Curriculum' describes the role of health education as "part of the preparation of the individual for personal, social and family responsibilities. Health education should give pupils a basic knowledge and understanding of health matters ... so that they are helped to make informed choices in their daily lives". In 1976, the DHSS consultative group on health education had already implied that "there is much potential for prevention in health education and in altering peoples' attitudes towards such things as tobacco, alcohol and exercise—persuading them in effect to invest in their own health". One of the largest secondary school health education projects is based upon these premises, namely the Schools Council/Health Education Council joint project 'Health Education 13-18' initiated in 1977, which has amongst its aims to give "young people a basic health knowledge and

understanding of human development" and to help them "determine where they have control over their health and where they can by conscious choices determine their future health and life style".

The fact that a number of today's prevalent health problems are associated with a sedentary lifestyle, therefore, raises questions about the possible contribution that physical education can make to an overall health education programme in helping children come to terms with informed decision-making processes concerning their present and future well-being. It seems that there is a danger of equating health in a physical education context to physical fitness, but as Haskell et al. (1985) state "becoming more physically fit and improving health status are interrelated, but they are not synonymous". In order to clarify what is meant here they provide an example to illustrate how endurance training *may* not produce the same benefits in terms of health

status and physical status; in talking about increases in aerobic capacity and the possible reduction in the risk of coronary heart disease they point out "the increase in aerobic capacity is likely due to an increase in oxygen transport and utilisation capacity, while a reduction in coronary heart disease risk may be the result of alterations in lipoprotein metabolism or fibrinolytic mechanisms such as blood-clotting". In this way, "... while the improvement in physical fitness and health may occur simultaneously during physical activity, the exercise-induced stimulus needed for each might be quite different". In fact there is little research evidence to support claims of a direct link between physical activity and the primary prevention of specific diseases; the data which exists tends to concentrate on the effects of exercise in secondary prevention, looking at specific biological changes thought to be connected with health status. The difficulty in providing a direct causal relationship between fitness and health is well illustrated by the paradox of the top class athlete: he or she can be highly 'tuned' for competition and can succeed in achieving outstanding results, and yet, simultaneously, the same individual can be medically classified as being in a state of ill-health, such as suffering from chronic asthma or a virus infection. Thus the role of physical education in health education is much broader than fitness *per se:* physical fitness (including aerobic capacity, muscle strength, flexibility) forms a part of a health focus, but the mental and physical well-being of a pupil encompasses the fostering of life long participation in activities of various kinds, and therefore the input from team games, racket games, swimming and so on is of equal importance in a health and physical education programme.

If one returns to the definition of 'health education', one of the major objectives therein is to provide pupils with a knowledge base from which they can make decisions determining their health behaviour. As far as physical education is concerned, one of the important contributions the subject can offer is an understanding of the effects of exercise on the body, and the associated benefits these can have in relation to health status. Children should realise that exercise helps to maintain the muscles, joints and the cardiovascular system in good working order, and enables the body to cope with moderate physical demands without undue fatigue. Obviously a basic understanding of the body's anatomy and physiology is valuable and some form of didactic interaction may be required initially to convey this information, but the practical nature of physical education ought to be capitalised upon to the full, and an exploration of the benefits of exercise will assume far greater meaning if the pupils learn through personal experience. For example, factual evidence outlining the fatal incidents of coronary heart disease in Britain *may* provide the necessary stimulus to interest children in preventative measures, but if the risk factors linked to the disease can be studied against a backcloth of practical activity, the likelihood of children adapting their attitudes towards methods of reducing those factors will be increased. Children must come to terms with the reality that appropriate exercise cannot 'wear the body out' but the body has in fact a magnificent capacity to respond to work loads by structural and physiological changes, and performance is enhanced by overload (Hardman, 1983). Regular exercise and sound nutrition must be seen to affect the body's capacity not merely within athletic performance but their value should also be shown in everday activities, such as running for a bus, climbing stairs, or carrying heavy goods. However, a practical knowledge base about health and exercise is virtually worthless in terms of health status unless children are keen to pursue activity regularly to facilitate the physiological and psychological benefits. Thus, whilst in many instances to date health and fitness work has been confined to the 4th and 5th year age range, physical educationalists must be aware of the need to foster positive attitudes towards activity from a very early age if life-time habits are to ensue. Fentem and Bassey (1978) write, "Parents and schools have an important role to play in fostering positive attitudes to exercise in all young people and not merely the sporting elite, in the hope that active lifestyles which are established early will last into maturity and old age".

The reference here to "the sporting elite" raises a critical issue in terms of health and physical education, and, as such, demands specific attention. At this point, it is appropriate to recognise the fact that a concern for health amongst physical educators is far from being a novel idea, and indeed many teachers would suggest that physical education has been providing pupils with a medium for health promotion for years; the experiences which children gain from physical education lessons form the basis on which they pursue leisure activities away from the school environment. Unfortunately there is increasing evidence that this belief is only true for a small minority of children and that many young people lead inactive lifestyles (Dickenson, 1985; Wilmore et al, 1981). One research study (Hill, 1984) revealed that at least 70 per cent of the physical education curriculum throughout one local education authority centred on competitive activities—namely team games and athletics—with the remainder of the programme being divided up between more individually-based activities such as gymnastics, dance and swimming. One can surmise that this is a reasonably typical representation of physical education curricula throughout the country, where the dominance of traditional team games has been a legacy from the late nineteenth century public school system based upon encouraging the qualities of discipline, courage and a sense of fair play through organised sport. Certainly the competitive experience is an important part of a child's education, and the skill acquisition required to participate in team games can contribute to a child's overall motor skill development. What is open to question however, is the seeming disproportionate amount of time dedicated to these ends, at the cost of other, equally beneficial, physical experiences. Many children feel a sense of constant failure when they fall short of the skill requirement needed in so many of the team games. Thomas (1985) cites this type of disillusionment when she quotes a woman reminiscing about her school days within a physical education context: ". . . You know sport isn't just for people brilliant at it, it's fun. That didn't really come over in school P.E. in my day . . . everything was about being top and being best, not about enjoying yourself at your own level". Belshaw (1982) writes, "We spend hundreds of hours teaching the skills of the major team games when, in fact, the vast majority of youngsters will not actively pursue these activities once they leave school." Biddle (1981) goes one step further to suggest "When

60 per cent of adults feel that their childhood exercise and activities were not applicable to them as adults then it appears that some form of change is needed". In other words, the critical factor is the child's experience of school physical education; if it is a bad experience this can affect the individual's self-concept and self-image (damaging to a pupil's development in itself), but moreover, painful memories of physical education lessons can have life-long implications for activity patterns and hence, implications for health status.

The debate surrounding the balance of the curriculum is thus central to encouraging children to be active, and the role of competitive games deserves further debate (see Sparkes, 1985 and Chapter 18). However, this chapter is concerned with a focus on health in physical education and thus it will return to this central

issue. In many ways, though, the factors are closely interlinked and the psychological aspects of a health focus are particularly entwined with competition. As already stated, successful failure can have serious consequences on a child's self-concept, but conversely, the sensation of success in competition can enhance self-esteem. In the past, many physical educationalists have seen competition as a driving motivational force, remembering that physical education teachers themselves have been a successful product in the competitive domain, but it seems increasingly the case that intrinsic satisfaction from activity is one of the most important influences in long-term participation, together with the desire to be with friends, i.e. affiliation as a motivation factor. One therefore has to assess which activities provide this type of affiliation opportunity and intrinsic satisfaction; indeed, how much physical kinesthesia is enjoyed in a game or skills programme related to hockey or football? Psychological analyses of the adherence problem have consequences for physical health in terms of participation, but it also has implications for mental health. Evidence is emerging to support the notion that exercise can induce mental well-being. "Feeling high" and relaxed, even after considerable physical exertion, is quite common amongst regular participants of activity, and it seems that these psychological side-effects may have their foundations in definite chemical changes in the state of the brain brought about by increased amines and endorphines during exercise. Reduced muscle tension via exercise can bring about similar emotions associated with a positive mental state. The fact that many children suffer from the traumas of Western urban living must mean that physical education cannot ignore the potential relief exercise can contribute to stressed youngsters. However, the determining factor related to the possible benefits is again dependent upon participation and enjoyable

experiences. If one takes the latter into account, it seems that a health focus in physical education should dedicate a considerable amount of time to individually-based activities, where children can benefit from an optimum level of activity and gain self-satisfaction from doing so. In this way, a reassessment of the balance in the curriculum could well mean a shift in focus away from team games towards greater use of racket sports, dance, swimming, gymnastics and so on. Furthermore, it also seems that it would be increasingly appropriate to develop the traditional 'cooling-down' period at the end of a lesson into a planned relaxation class, in order to 'physically' educate children about coping with stress. On the other side of the psychological coin is the fact that some people actually derive satisfaction from being in a controlled stressful situation; indeed the boredom factor in many individuals' lives can be equally harmful to their well-being, as can a state of stress. In this instance, therefore, the role of competitive activities, where the amount of stress experienced can be controlled to a greater degree, can be 'healthy' to an individual, and thus here is another way in which physical education can contribute to a health programme.

In sketching out the health focus in physical education, therefore, there are a number of important issues to consider. Education in its entirety is concerned about the development of the individual—mentally, physically and socially—and physical education has much to offer all three of these areas. Physical and mental well-being, together with good health, are central to the quality of an individual's life, becoming increasingly important as the ageing process takes its toll. Whilst old age and its associated infirmity and debilitation appears to be out of young peoples' conceptual reach, physical educators must ensure that measures are taken early on in the maturation process to encourage good long-term lifestyle habits. Moreover, young people must be afforded the opportunity to enhance their current lifestyles via the benefits of regular exercise and participation in a variety of activities. Indeed, physical education lessons should provide children with a broad physical experience from which they can choose activities to pursue in their own time, and similarly, the programme should provide them with the necessary knowledge to enable them to assume responsibility for their health and general well-being. As Corbin (personal communication, December 1985) states, physical education in the past has tended towards the highly structured environment and this has resulted in children being highly dependent upon the structure for activity; children have the right and capability to be responsible for their own activity patterns, hence, he argues, physical education must lead children from dependence to independence. In other words, at some stage in the physical education programme pupils must be encouraged to make personal decisions about the type of activity in which they participate, they must have a broad experience on which to base their decision-making, and, perhaps most important of all, if their participation is to be beneficial, particularly in the long-term, then the physical experience must be an enjoyable one. A health focus in physical education encompasses the positive physical and mental attributes of physical health and physical education, but a focus of health centres on the quality of the physical experience and hence the entire programme has a contribution to make in promoting young peoples' well-being.

References

BELSHAW, P. (1982). Setting the scene, mapping the ground and outlining the task. *The role of physical education in the whole curriculum.* DES Regional Course, B.3, 20. Elm Bank Teachers' Centre.

BIDDLE, S. (1981). The Why of health-related fitness. *Bulletin of Physical Education,* Vol. 17 (3).

Department of Education and Science (1981). *The school curriculum.* London: HMSO.

Department of Health and Social Security (1976). *Prevention and health: everybody's business.* London: HMSO.

DICKENSON, B. (1985). Unpublished M.Phil thesis, Loughborough University of Technology.

FENTEM, P.H. and BASSEY, E.J. (1978). *The case for exercise.* Sports Council Research Workshop Papers No. 8.

HARDMAN, A. (1983). Practical projects for teachers. *Bulletin of Physical Education,* Vol. 19 (2).

HASKELL, W.L., MONTOYE, H.J. and ORENSTEIN, D. (1985). Physical activity and exercise to achieve health-related physical fitness components. *Public Health Reports,* Vol. 100 (2).

HILL, C. (1984). Unpublished M.Phil thesis, Loughborough University of Technology.

McCAFFERTY, I. (1979). Health education in the education system. In D.C. Anderson (Ed.). *Health education in practice.* London: Croom Helm.

MITCHELL, R.G. (1982). Benefits of leisure stress. *Journal of Physical Education, Recreation and Dance,* Vol. 53 (7).

Schools Council/Health Education Council (1984). *Health education 13-18 project: developing health education – a co-ordinator's guide.* London: Forbes Publications.

SPARKES, A. (1985). The competitive mansion – built on sand. *British Journal of Physical Education,* Vol. 16 (2)

THOMAS, J. (1985). Remembrance of things past and best forgotten. *Physical Education Review,* Vol. 8 (1).

WILMORE, J.H., CONSTABLE, S.H., STANFORTH, P.R., TSAO W.Y., ROTKIS, T.C., PANCIUS, R.M. and MALTERN, C.P. (1981). Coronary artery disease risk factors in 13 to 15 year old boys. *Medicine and Science in Sports and Exercise,* 13 (1).

Chapter Three

Health and Fitness Programmes in Schools: A Physiological Rationale

Neil Armstrong

Why Implement a Health and Fitness Programme?

We live in a sedentary culture and although the battle against infectious diseases is being won the occurrence of hypokinetic diseases—those related to or caused by the lack of regular physical activity—continues to rise at an alarming rate.

For example, in the United Kingdom 88,000 adults are unable to work each day because of back pain. Twenty six million working days are lost through backache every year at a cost to the nation of one thousand million pounds in medical care, sickness benefit and lost production. The cost to the individual and his/her family in personal suffering is impossible to estimate. Even more serious is the tragedy of atherosclerotic coronary heart disease which is annually responsible for the death of 180,000 Britons. In other Western countries the toll from atherosclerosis is steadily declining, but not in the United Kingdom. Consider the American experience where, in 1968, an American middle aged man had a 40% greater chance of dying from ischaemic coronary heart disease than an Englishman, yet, by 1976, after a huge education and intervention programme in the United States, the American figures were actually lower than the figures in England and Wales. British doctors are the only members of our society whose mortality from ischaemic heart disease has gone down (Anon, 1980).

How relevant is this information to the physical education teacher? I suggest that it is highly relevant as there is a growing conviction among doctors and scientists that hypokinetic diseases are a paediatric problem. This premise can be substantiated by considering atherosclerotic coronary heart disease which the World Health Organisation (1971) claims to be potentially the greatest epidemic the world has ever faced.

Blood is supplied to the heart by the coronary arteries and if flow through these vessels

becomes restricted there is danger of a heart attack. Atherosclerosis is basically the narrowing of the lumen of the coronary arteries and in addition to the narrowing effect the afflicted arteries often become stiff or hardened (arteriosclerosis). The narrowing is progressive and in advanced stages the blood flow through the artery can be completely stopped. When this occurs that part of the heart muscle supplied with blood by the artery "dies"—a heart attack. The severity of the heart attack is determined by the exact location of the block within the artery.

The artherosclerotic lesion involves intimal smooth muscle proliferation, increase of arterial connective tissue, an accumulation of lipids within the intima and a collection of other materials including fibrin, blood cells and platelets. The initial lesion in the arterial wall starts as an accumulation of lipid and results in non-elevated fatty streaks under the inner lining. What is not widely appreciated is that these streaks have been found in the aortas of children 3 to 4 months old. By the age of 5 years they are relatively common and are features by the age of 10 years. Fatty streaks become evident in the coronary arteries during the second decade of life and regardless of geographic or ethnic origin most people have developed coronary artery fatty streaks by the age of 20 years (Armstrong and Davies, 1980a). The fibrous plaque which first appears during adolescence is a raised atherosclerotic lesion with a potential for narrowing the arterial lumen and causing the complications of progressive atherosclerotic disease. The progression from fatty streaks through fibrous plaques to athermatous ulceration cannot be documented by longitudinal studies in human subjects. However, recent evidence demonstrating an intermediate stage between the fatty streaks and the plaque (Small, 1977) and an accumulation of cross-sectional data supports the belief that the embryo of atherosclerosis commences early in life and is catalysed by certain so-called coronary risk factors.

Coronary risk factors have been defined as, "those abnormalities demonstrable in persons free of clinical coronary heart disease and known to be associated with significantly increased risk of developing the disease in subsequent years" (Stamler et al, 1966). The disclosure of a risk factor does not prove a causal relationship between the risk factor and the atherosclerotic complications but several intervention studies have shown that a reduction in the risk factor causes a reduction in the incidence of atherosclerotic disease. It is therefore reasonable to conclude that individuals displaying several risk factors at an early age are potential coronary candidates.

The primary risk factors have been identified as hyperlipidaemia (especially high serum cholesterol), hypertension and cigarette smoking. Secondary factors include obesity, physical inactivity, positive family history of premature vascular disease and various other less well established phenomena ranging from stress level to caffeine intake. People displaying a combination of these risk factors have a susceptibility to coronary heart disease which is increased by a factor substantially greater than the sum of their individual contributions. In earlier papers we reviewed the prevalence of coronary risk factors in children and established that the risk factors commonly identified in adults are frequently present in children (Armstrong and Davies, 1980a, 1980b).

Primary Risk Factors
High Serum Cholesterol
There is no safe level of cholesterol and regardless of age or sex it is generally accepted that the lower the serum cholesterol level the better. Nevertheless a critical level below which risk of premature coronary artery disease would not be likely has been established as 5.20 mmol/l and children with serum cholesterol levels in excess of this critical value have been regularly identified. Detailed scrutiny of the published data to date reveals that 1 in 4 of the children examined have serum cholesterol levels exceeding this criterion. Recent evidence, however, suggests that this is too simplistic an analysis and that in addition to the total cholesterol its distribution among the lipoproteins is critical (Armstrong and Davies, 1982). Low density lipoprotein cholesterol (LDL-C) and high density lipoprotein cholesterol (HDL-C) together reflect the total serum cholesterol level, but it is LDL-C which contributes to the atherosclerotic process and HDL-C is becoming recognised as conferring antiatherogenic properties. HDL-C interferes with the binding and uptake of LDL-C at extrahepatic tissues and facilitates the transport of cholesterol from peripheral tissues to the liver for subsequent catabolism and excretion as bile acids or free cholesterol. Differences in sampling procedure and analytical variation in the estimation of lipoprotein levels makes data

collected in different studies very difficult to interpret and comparative reference values for HDL-C will not be uniformly established until analytical protocols have been standardised (Armstrong and Davies, 1982). Nevertheless, it is worth noting that after assessing a strictly random sample of 308 boys (13-15 years) Wilmore and his associates (1981) concluded that 30% of the boys had HDL-C levels compatible with coronary risk.

It has been clearly shown that increasing amounts of dietary saturated fats elevate the serum cholesterol level while polyunsaturated fats decrease it. Cholesterol restriction and an alteration of the polyunsaturated to saturated fat ratio results in significant decreases of the serum cholesterol level. Furthermore a consistent finding in adult studies is that sustained, vigorous aerobic exercise increases HDL-C levels. The data linking exercise with increased HDL-C concentrations in children are not unequivocal but evidence is accumulating to support the premise that regular, intensive exercise during childhood will promote favourable changes in plasma lipoprotein patterns (see Armstrong and Davies, 1982).

Hypertension

As with cholesterol there does not appear to be a simple critical level and the greater the blood pressure the greater the atherosclerotic risk. As it is known that blood pressure rises with age any adult criteria are probably inappropriate for use with children. However, since estimates suggest that approximately 20% of adults have blood pressure levels placing them at risk it seems reasonable to suppose that children with blood pressures greater than the 80th percentile for their age may eventually prove to be hypertensive adults.

Although much of the evidence available at the present time must be interpreted with caution because of numerous methodological shortcomings, a recent well designed study by Hagberg et al (1983) clearly demonstrated the value of aerobic exercise in the reduction of the arterial blood pressure of hypertensive children.

Cigarette smoking

The United Kingdom has the world's highest death rate from lung cancer and it has been estimated that 55,000 men and 22,000 women in England and Wales die each year solely because they smoke. Although there has been a reduction in adult smoking since the late 1970s recent reports indicate a 3% increase in school-children's smoking since 1982 (Physical Education Association, 1986). About half of all boys and a third of all girls have tried their first cigarette by the age of 11 years but it is during adolescence that the habit takes a firm hold and children aged between 11 and 16 manage to smoke about £60 million worth of cigarettes per annum. The largest increase in smoking is among adolescent girls and evidence from some parts of the country suggests that smoking is now more prevalent among 15 to 16 year old girls than among boys of the same age (Wilcox and Gillies, 1984). By the age of 16 years about 27% of British schoolchildren are regular smokers (Dobbs and Marsh, 1983).

Anti-smoking educational programmes

should begin at an early age with a high priority for the 11 to 13 age group and programmes based on education for personal growth are probably preferable to purely information-giving approaches (Reid, 1985). As smoking severely restricts aerobic performance frequent exposure to the adverse effects of smoking on the cardiorespiratory system may help to motivate children to adopt more prudent habits.

Secondary Risk Factors
Obesity

Due to the difficulties in estimating children's body composition and the fact that no universally accepted criterion exists as to what specific percentage of body fat constitutes obesity in children, the prevalence of childhood obesity has been reported to vary from 2.5% to 28%. In the United Kingdom 5% to 6% of children can be classified as obese—on average one child in every class. The evidence of a marked increase in childhood obesity in recent years is overwhelming and longitudinal data have demonstrated the remarkable persistence of obesity, with 70% to 80% of obese children developing into obese adults.

The success of balanced nutrition and aerobic exercise programmes in the prevention and rehabilitation of obesity is well established (see Armstrong and Davies, 1982 and chapters 7 and 8).

Physical inactivity

Children are very willing laboratory subjects and it is relatively easy to determine maximal cardiorespiratory parameters using ergometry (Armstrong and Davies, 1984). The use of ergometric tests, however, provides limited insight into children's physical activity patterns and only through continuous observation and recording over an extended period of time can free living physical activity be quantified and an understanding of its determinants developed. The problems involved in examining physical activity patterns have been identified and data concerned with the habitual physical activity of schoolchildren are accumulating (Armstrong and Davies, 1982). Unfortunately the evidence indicates that children are not as active as they appear and that habitual activity is seldom of high enough intensity to promote cardiovascular health. Furthermore as children leave the school environment, leisure time physical activity tends to decrease, especially among girls. Recent studies have reported the percentage of inactive children to range from 3 to 35. The higher figure is based on data obtained from a strictly random sample of 308 boys (Wilmore et al, 1981), and is therefore perhaps a more realistic estimate of the population value as most samples tend to be convenience samples which often exclude "unfit" children. As indicated above, data are difficult to interpret because there is no agreed criterion below which a child is universally regarded as "inactive", but some individual studies are worthy of note. Seliger et al (1974) monitored a group of 12 year old boys and found that heart rates of over 150 were rare and only fleetingly encountered. They concluded that very little circulatory activity was required to support the boys' daily activity. Bradfield et al (1971) demonstrated that high school girls spent 70% of their time either in sleep or very light activities. Ilmarinen and Rutenfranz (1980) followed 25 girls and 26 boys for four years and

observed a marked decrease in sporting activities with age. Gilliam et al (1981), using Holter monitoring, reported that 7 year old boys and girls achieved heart rates greater than 159 for only 21 and 9 minutes respectively during a 12-hour period.

It is therefore highly probable that schoolchildren share many of the sedentary habits of their parents and teachers and that few experience the intensity, frequency and duration of physical activity that is required to foster the development of a strong healthy heart.

Multiple risk factors

Combinations of risk factors may also occur during childhood and presumably carry an increased risk as in adults. There is, however, a dearth of studies identifying multiple risk factors in children, although reports from America suggest that in their society only just over a third of children are free from all risk factors. One study reported that 20% of the sample exhibited 3 risks factors, 10% exhibited 4 risk factors and one child exhibited 5 risk factors (Gilliam et al, 1977). No major studies have been reported in the United Kingdom but recent pilot work from my laboratory supports the American findings. We are currently undertaking work which should help to clarify the scope of the problem in the United Kingdom.

Atherosclerosis usually becomes clinically manifest in adult life but the evidence outlined above strongly indicates that it has its origins in childhood and that the only way to substantially alter its course is to attack its constitutional and environmental precursors before overt signs and symptoms occur.

How can the Physical Education Teacher combat hypokinetic disease

Physical education teachers need to emphasise the importance of health and fitness in the school curriculum. Health and fitness programmes designed to change the lifestyles of children, their parents and their teachers must be initiated. Ideally such a project should involve collaboration with other teachers, parents, advisers, in Institutes of Higher Education, medical and paramedical personnel. In the United States several successful projects of this type have been developed but even without a multifaceted group programme the physical educator can still make a significant contribution by designing courses which actively promote positive changes in children's attitude to exercise and associated activities.

When should Health and Fitness be introduced?

The seeds of health and fitness should be planted in the primary school and children should be encouraged to adopt active lifestyles from an early age. Health education, nutrition education and human biology should all be introduced at this stage and the Health Education Council has some excellent resources available for use in schools.

In the secondary school health and fitness should underpin the physical education curriculum and the emphasis should be placed upon a range of sports and activites which can persist into adult life. It should be clearly demonstrated that exercise can be enjoyable and that competition and/or athletic excellence are not necesary for the maintenance of physical fitness and health. How many children have been discouraged through lack of competitive success simply because their biological clock ran more slowly than their classmates? Children need to be exposed to a variety of activities, not just sport, and early specialisation is usually achieved at the expense of developing a broader base of fundamental motor skills.

Astrand et al's (1963) comprehensive study of 30 young female swimmers aptly illustrates the potential outcome of exposing young children to chronic, intensive, specific training. It was demonstrated that both functional and dimensional measures of cardiorespiratory fitness may be improved by long-term swim training. The girls developed significantly larger lung volumes, blood volumes, heart volumes and total haemoglobin than untrained girls of corresponding body size, and the increased dimensions correlated well with the increases in maximum aerobic power. However, this study was followed up ten years later (Eriksson et al, 1971) and by this time all the girls had stopped swimming and most did not engage in any physical activity in their spare time. All of the girls showed a decrease in maximal aerobic power which was on average 29% and took

them to a value some 15% below the mean for Swedish females of the same age. Apparently, as the dimensions of their cardiorespiratory systems remained enlarged, the girls retained the organic capacity for high levels of aerobic work even though their maximal oxygen uptakes had significantly decreased due to their markedly reduced activity level. The impression left is that the girl swimmers were "turned off" to activity as adults. In spite of their physiological advantages they were functioning at levels below average for women of the same age. Could it be that early specialisation and lack of variety—perhaps also lack of understanding, knowing the "how?" of exericse without knowing the "why?"—had turned them off exercise during adulthood?

From the age of 14 (fourth year) special provision should be made for the inclusion of health and fitness in the school curriculum. Physical education teachers should lobby for extra time and resources in order to mount a comprehensive programme. The "powers that be"—head teachers, advisers, senior colleagues—should be made aware of the fact that hypokinetic diseases, particularly coronary heart disease, are of paediatric origin and must be tackled during childhood. Some of us have already won the battle for extra time for examination courses in physical education and for the inclusion of additional physical education in sixth-form general studies programmes, and we know that the struggle for increased time can be won with a lot of perseverence and a little support from the right quarter. In the meantime space should be made available within the physical education programmes of older children and young adults to promote health and fitness more explicitly.

What should be included in a Health and Fitness course?

Teachers must concentrate on changing children's attitudes to exercise and initiating a

lifetime commitment to physical activity and healthy eating. It is not enough to simply increase the activity level of lessons or even the number of active sessions as several studies have demonstrated that this has a minimal effect on most young children (see Armstong and Davies, 1984). Youngsters must be helped to understand the principles underlying health and fitness and taught how to develop and monitor their own individual fitness programme which can be periodically re-appraised and modified as they grow older.

If health and fitness courses are to be meaningful they must be based on an experiential learning approach and although each teacher will develop his/her own strategies and approaches it is imperative that the course is practically based and involves practical and experimental work in the gymnasium, on the playing fields and in the classroom laboratory. A comprehensive course should include the following:

The concept of fitness
Health-related fitness
Skill-related fitness
Fitness for life

Muscular Energy
Definition of energy
The generation of muscular energy (aerobic/anaerobic)
The sources of muscular energy (fats/carbohydrates/proteins)

Exercise and health
Heart disease and other hypokinetic conditions
Body mechanics
Back care

Posture guidelines
Stress, tension and relaxation
Abuse diseases, smoking, alcohol and other drugs
Surreptitious advertising

Principles of exercise and training
Safety factors
Warm-up and cool-down
Planning a training programme
Principles of exercise and training (overload, progression, specificity)
Methods of evaluating training programmes
Long-term effects of training

Cardiorespiratory fitness
Functions of the cardiorespiratory system
Response to the cardiorespiratory system to exercise of varying type, duration and intensity
Development of cardiorespiratory fitness
Evaluation of cardiorespiratory fitness

Body Composition
Dietary and nutritional requirements (balanced diets)
Weight control (ideal body weight, energy balance)
Obesity (aetiology, prevention and treatment)
Evaluation of body composition

Muscular fitness
Development of muscular strength and endurance
Factors affecting muscular strength and endurance
Evaluation of muscular strength and endurance

Flexibility
  Development of flexibility
  Factors affecting flexibility
  Evaluation of flexibility

Looking good
  Personal hygiene
  Skin care
  Hair care
  Feet care
  Self projection

Exercise, leisure and the community
  Sports clubs and related organisations
  Leisure activities
  Available activities

It will also be necessary for some children to appreciate the interaction of exercise and diet with disabilities and injuries, e.g. asthma, diabetes, epilepsy and joint injuries.

Are Physical Education Teachers equipped to teach Health and Fitness courses?

If teachers are to develop worthwhile courses they must have a good understanding of the theory and practice of movement science. Many teachers have the necessary background and several institutions (e.g. Exeter University) already include health and fitness as a major component of their undergraduate programme, but it is likely that some teachers will feel that their training did not adequately prepare them for work of this type.

Universities, colleges and polytechnics must be willing to provide relevant in-service courses and LEAs must be prepared to support this development. Advisers should consider using the Teacher Fellowship scheme to pool the cost of seconding a member of staff to an institution of higher education with expertise in this field. Following the Fellowship the teacher would be in a position to help other staff to develop appropriate courses and to lead an area team. Resource centres could be established with pooled equipment and course packs which could be loaned to schools when required.

Will society benefit from the introduction of Health and Fitness programmes in schools?

If we, as physical educators, can offer the example of a fit, non-smoking, healthy eating and moderately drinking profession, if we can influence children's attitudes to exercise so that they leave school with a repertoire of movement skills, a love for a variety of exercise and a realisation that they are never too old to exercise, and if children leave school with the knowledge to enable them to maintain cardiovascular health, muscular fitness, optimal flexibility and to "make the most of themselves", then our contribution to society may well be to add years to life and life to years.

References
ANONYMOUS, (1980). Why the American decline in coronary heart disease? *Lancet*.
ARMSTRONG, N. and DAVIES, B. (1980a) Coronary risk factors in children. *Acta Paediatrica Belgica*, Vol. 33.
ARMSTRONG, N. and DAVIES, B. (1980b) Coronary risk factors in children—the role of the physical educator. *Bulletin of Physical Education*, Vol. 16.
ARMSTRONG, N. and DAVIES, B. (1982) High density lipoprotein cholesterol and physical activity patterns in children. *Australian Journal of Sports Medicine*, Vol. 14.
ARMSTRONG, N. and DAVIES, B. (1984) The metabolic and physiological responses of children to exercise and training. *Physical Education Review*, Vol. 7.
ASTRAND, P.O., ENGSTROM, L., ERIKSSON, B.O., KARLBERG, P., NYLANDER, I., SALTIN, B. and THOREN, C. (1963). Girl Swimmers. *Acta Paediatrica*, Vol. 147.
BREDFIELD, R.B., PAULOS, J. and CROSSMAN, L., (1971). Energy expenditure and heart rate of obese high school girls, *American Journal of Clinical Nutrition*, Vol. 24
DOBBS, J. and MARSH, A., (1983). *Smoking Among Secondary Schoolchildren*. London, H.M.S.O.
ERIKSSON, B.O., ENGSTROM, I., KARLBERG, P., SALTIN, B. and THOREN, C. (1971) A physiological analysis of former girl swimmers. *Acta Paediatrica Scandanavia*, Suppl. 217.
GILLIAM, T.B., KATCH, V.L., THORLAND, W. and WELTMAN, A. (1977). Prevalence of coronary heart disease risk factors in active children 7-12 years of age. *Medicine and*

Science in Sports, Vol. 9.

GILLIAM, T.B., FREEDSON, P.S., GEENED, P.L. and SHAHRARAY, B. (1981). Physical activity patterns determined by heart rate monitoring in 6 to 7 year old children. *Medicine and Science in Sports and Exercise,* Vol. 13.

HAGBERG, J.M., GOLDRING, D., EHSANI, A.A., HEATH, G.W., HERNANDEZ, A., SCHECHTMAN, K. and HOLLOSZY, J.O. (1983). Effect of exercise training on the blood pressure and hemodynamic features of hypertensive adolescents. *American Journal of Cardiology,* Vo. 52.

ILMARINEN, J. and RUTENFRANZ, J. (1980). Longitundinal studies of the changes in habitual physical activity of schoolchildren and working adolescents. In K. Berg and B.O. Eriksson (eds), *Children and Exercise 1X,* Baltimore: University Park Press.

Physical Education Association (1986). Dramatic increase in child smokers. *British Journal of Physical Education,* Vol. 17.

REID, D. (1985). Prevention of smoking among schoolchildren: Recommendations for policy development. *Health Education Journal,* Vol. 44.

SELIGER, V. TREFNY, S., BARTUNKOVA, S. and PAUER, M. (1974). The habitual activity and physical fitness of 12 year old boys. *Acta Paediatrica Belgica,* Vol. 28.

SMALL, D.M. (1977). Cellular mechanisms for lipid deposition in atherosclerosis. *Journal of the American Medical Association,* Vol. 297.

STAMLER, J. BERKSON, D.M., LINDBERG, H.A., HALLY, Y., MILLER, W., MOGONNIER, L., LEVINSON, M., COHEN, D.B. and YOUNG, O.D. (1966). Coronary risk factors. *Medical Clinics of North America,* Vol. 50.

WILCOX, B. and GILLIES, P. (1984). Prevalence of smoking among schoolchildren in Sheffield. *Health Education Journal,* Vol. 43.

WILMORE, J.H., CONSTABLE, S.H., STANFORTH, P.R., TSAE, W.Y., ROTKIS, T.C., PAUCIUS, R.M. and MALTERN, C.P. (1981). Coronary artery disease risk factors in 13 to 15 year old boys. *Medicine and Science in Sports and Exercise,* Vol. 13.

World Health Organisation (1971). Executive Board 27, February 1969. *British Heart Journal,* Vol. 33.

An earlier version of this chapter appeared in the *British Journal of Physical Education,* Vol. 15(6), under the title "Why implement a health-related fitness programme?"

SECTION B

Components of Health-Related Fitness

Chapter Four

Cardiovascular Fitness and the Curriculum

Ken Fox & Charles Corbin

In chapter 1, we made a strong attempt to show the necessity for the teaching of health-related fitness in schools. It was emphasised that while 'fitness for the present' objectives are important, we must not allow them to overshadow 'fitness for life' goals for schoolchildren. A major aim of physical education programmes should be to equip ALL students with fitness problem-solving skills as well as positive attitudes towards involvement in physical activity. In the long term, this objective will enhance the chances of our students achieving lifetime fitness and health.

The following chapters of ours (5, 6 and 7), will overview basic information which will aid teachers in presenting the important aspects of each component of health-related fitness as they apply to the curriculum. This first one will focus on cardiovascular fitness. In it we will try to answer the questions: WHY should cardiovascular fitness promotion be a fundamental part of the programme? WHAT do students need to know about cardiovascular fitness? and HOW is the programme best able to promote lifetime cardiovascular fitness in students?

Why teach cardiovascular fitness?

We are all familiar with the nature of cardiovascular functioning. Put simply, it is the ability of the heart, lungs, blood vessels, and working muscle cells to work effectively and efficiently. Progressively increased exercise or 'overload' on this system will cause an adaptation and a resultant increase in cardiovascular work capacity. In other words, exercise which raises the heart rate and breathing sufficiently for long enough periods of time will, if done frequently enough, lead to a fit cardiovascular system.

Of all the parts, cardiovascular fitness is probably the most important for overall health and well-being. The benefits of cardiovascular fitness are great and it should be the central

feature of any exercise programme. People who are involved in regular aerobic or cardiovascular activity such as jogging or aerobic dance, report benefits which fall into three broad categories, each of which has substantial confirmation by research evidence.

First, a fit cardiovascular system is more resilient to coronary heart disease (CHD) and other circulatory problems such as hypertension, stroke, and varicose veins. CHD is the leading cause of death in Britain, and at a time when some countries are seeing reductions in these conditions, our disease rate is one of the highest in the world and continues to climb. After years of collecting evidence associating regular exercise with a reduced incidence of heart disease, causal link has now been declared by the medical profession (Paffenbarger et. al., 1984). The protective benefits of exercise are twofold. Large scale studies of whole communities have shown that with regular activity, there is a reduction in the CHD risk factors such as improved blood fat profile, lowered diastolic blood pressure (among those with hypertension), and reduction in stress levels.

Furthermore, a small reduction in one or more of these risk factors appears to make a big difference in reduction in mortality rate and chances of having a premature heart attack. In addition to risk reduction, regular aerobic exercise results in a stronger and more efficient circulatory system. Muscle cells become more active users of oxygen and there is increase capillarisation in the working muscles. This is particularly significant in the heart muscle itself where it is known as coronary collateral circulation. The result of these physiological changes is a heart system that has improved work capacity and greater ability to survive heart attacks.

The second benefit of cardiovascular exercise lies in the effect it has on helping people to look better. For example, few regular joggers are overfat, even though many start out that way. Cardiovascular work typically involves large muscle groups which burn up lots of calories and the accompanying fat loss, muscle firmness, and an overall look of health and vitality are frequently reported by aerobic exercisers. Looking good is a benefit which adolescents in particular, readily identify with and value.

Finally, cardiovascular activity is the mode of exercise most frequently associated with feeling good, a state of well-being which either occurs during or following the exercise. Some experience pleasant feelings or a 'high' while exercising. Others are relieved when it is over, but then enjoy warm relaxing sensations and feelings of fulfilment which tend to last for hours afterwards. Evidence suggests that the activity has to be of sufficient intensity (60% to 80% of maximum) and duration (20 to 30 minutes) for these sensations to be really appreciated. In addition, regular activity often leads to feelings of mastery and competence over the physical environment which can result in enhancement of self-esteem. These aspects of feeling good are important because they tend to be most successful in motivating people to adhere to their regular exercise programme, and 'feeling good' is frequently given as the prime reason for continuing exercising.

The rationale for the inclusion of cardiovascular fitness education is substantial as it can offer tremendous benefits to the welfare of the individual and the nation. Recent studies have shown that coronary risk factors are present in most American schoolchildren, and the higher incidence of heart disease in Britain would suggest a similar pattern in British schoolkids as well as adults. In the long term, encouragement of lifetime aerobic exercise in schools will help reduce premature death, suffering, and health expense. The good news is that programmes which have already attempted this have reported great successes (Kuntzleman, 1984; Slava, Laurie & Corbin, 1984).

What do students need to know about cardiovascular fitness?

As children pass through their school years, they should acquire both knowledge and skills regarding cardiovascular fitness.

Knowledge and Understanding

Knowledge and understanding provide the key to intelligent decision-making. We shouldn't expect students to be convinced about the worth of cardiovascular exercise without a sound knowledge base. If students are aware of the benefits of cardiovascular activity that we have already discussed, their attitudes and motives will be strengthened. Information alone CAN change behaviour. An understanding of the short term and chronic physiological changes caused by cardiovascular exercise, the mechanisms and symptoms of coronary heart disease, the link between exercise and other coronary risk factors, and the role played by aerobic exercise in weight control are all prime areas for attention which can be presented in an interesting and stimulating format. Add this to an understanding of the psychological benefits of regular activity, and the student is more likely to feel the need to incorporate cardiovascular activity into his/her lifestyle.

Health-related Skills

Unlike sport and movement skills which are basically motoric, health-related skills tend to be thinking and decision-making skills. If we refer back to the 'stairway to lifetime fitness' (see chapter 1), we see that higher-order health-related skills allow the individual to solve personal fitness problems. If the school experience is to have a lifetime effect, the acquisition of this type of skill should receive attention in the curriculum.

Self-testing and self-monitoring skills are fundamental for the diagnosis of fitness needs throughout life. Also, fitness tests and stunts are an excellent means of introducing and elucidating some of the more important concepts by way of the 'Experimental' approach advocated by Almond (1983).

There are many standardised tests of cardiovascular fitness available. Some are simple and some more sophisticated. Some only give good "estimates" of fitness status while others are more precise. The criterion measure of cardiovascular performance, or aerobic power as it is often called, is the test of maximal oxygen uptake (max. V02) involving all-out performance usually on a treadmill or bicycle ergometer. This takes place in a laboratory and requires complex gas collection and analysis equipment which these days is often computerised. More suitable but less accurate

alternatives are available for the school and individual which are not only easier and less time consuming, but which can also be used for self-assessment throughout life.

The simplest of test is the old faithful step test which bases its estimate of cardiovascular fitness on heart rate recovery time after exercising has ceased. The fittest individuals recover most rapidly. Although this test is not a particularly good predictor of maximal oxygen uptake, it is very useful in a class or gymnasium setting for demonstrating fitness principles and learning the various forms of heart rate monitoring.

The 12-minute or 1.5 mile walk/run for older students and the 9-minute or 1 mile walk/run for the younger children are very useful field tests of cardiovascular performance which under the right circumstances can also be very good indicators of maximal oxygen uptake. They can be performed on an individual self-test basis or with large numbers of students in class. The tests simply measure distance covered or time taken for a specific distance when running or walking as fast as possible. Caution should be taken to make sure that students are ready to take this type of test. To require students to take a test early in the school year without prior training or pacing practice, and without full explanation regarding the purpose and need for the test, is unwise.

Some schools may eventually be able to afford bicycle ergometers (approximately £400 each) which can be used for the sub-maximal estimation of maximal oxygen uptake. Subjects heart rate response to the bicycle workload is measured by frequently checking the pulse rate. When a steady state heart rate has been achieved, performance of the subject at maximum workload can be predicted. Although it is dificult to test large numbers of students in a short period, bicycle tests have proved excellent for the demonstration of the relationship between exercise intensity and heart rate, blood pressure, and perceptions of exertion in the classroom setting. The tests described here are dealt with in more detail elsewhere (AAHPERD, 1983; Corbin & Lindsey, 1985; see chapter 15).

Exercise prescription skills.

Perhaps most important of all, students should learn how to plan their own exercise programmes. The ability to plan a cardiovascular fitness programme which can be used for a lifetime is a culminating experience in a cardiovascular fitness unit. Once students have learned to self test, they will have a good idea of their needs. Then they are ready to learn basic principles of exercise prescription.

The question, "How much exercise is enough?", can be answered through application of the F. I. T. principle. Here the F stands for Frequency, the I for Intensity, and the T for Time. To build cardiovascular fitness, exercise frequency should be 3 to 6 days a week, exercise intensity should be great enough to elevate the heart rate to 60-80% of maximum, and exercise time should be at least 30 minutes each time a person exercises. The minimum frequency, intensity, and time (duration) of exercise which will produce cardiovascular fitness gains is called the "threshold of training". The optimal range of training is considered to be the cardiovascular target zone for fitness training. Exercise done in excess of the target zone (for example, more than 6 days a week) may result in increased chance of injury and may be uncomfortable of unenjoyable.

Just as students need an accurate awareness of the amount of exercise necessary for training, they should have an understanding, based on the F. I. T. principle, of which sports and activities can help promote and maintain their cardiovascular health. For example: Will two games of soccer each week be effective in meeting cardiovascular requirements? Will activities such as walking, swimming, weight-training or aerobic dance promote cardiovascular fitness? Students need to learn to answer questions such as these. In this regard, a clear grasp of the differences between the two modes of cardiovascular training, known as aerobic and anaerobic exercise, is necessary. The advantages and disadvantages of each, and the part they play in performing each activity, should be understood by every student.

It is important that the basic principles of progression and overload also be understood by our students. These principles have particular significance for the beginning exerciser who tends to progress and overload too quickly causing either soreness or injury. In this regard we would also make students aware of the need for cardiovascular warm-up and cool-down, and work them into an overall programme of fitness.

In effect, the product of our cardiovascular fitness provision should be students who at least have the knowledge, understanding and skills to enable them to design cardiovascular exercise for themselves which is safe, free from gimickry, effective, and above all, enjoyable. The information and concepts presented in this section have only briefly been discussed for the

sake of space but are presented in more detail elsewhere (Bassey & Fentem, 1982; Corbin & Lindsey, 1982, 1985).

How can the programme best promote lifetime cardiovascular fitness in students?

There is no one definitive format for the presentation of the previously discussed material in the physical education programme. It is evident that every school situation has unique aspects that will influence the exact means of implementation. In particular there are important developmental considerations so the primary school provision will be substantially different to that of secondary schools. One attempt to develop a health-related fitness programme at secondary level has already been described in detail (see chapter 11).

In the short term, we know that most youngsters are more concerned with the present than future health outlook. To some extent our youth may feel a sense of 'immortality'. For this reason they may perceive that the protection benefit of exercise is of limited immediate importance to them and only concerns 'older' people. For motivation purposes, the benefits of looking and feeling better along with improvement of quality of life can be emphasised. With very young children who have limited capacity to abstract the notion of

future wellness, the instant incentive of fun and enjoyment should receive priority when cardiovascular activities are presented. Above all, the objective at all levels should be to create pleasant association with exercise for children so that they grow with positive attitudes.

With this fundamental goal in mind, we briefly present the following guidelines concerning the programme and student/teacher interface.

1. To give students a reasonable chance of enjoying cardiovascular activity at secondary level, the programme must offer a broader range of choice than is usual. The most popular adult fitness pursuits are walking, jogging, swimming, and cycling, and more recently, aerobic dance. If this is what people do, given freedom of choice, there must be good reason. Although many sports such as soccer or basketball are excellent for the promotion of cardiovascular fitness, other non-competitive and individually-orientated options should be available for students. Examples of activities which have proved successful have been aerobic dance, beginning or continuing jogging classes, and swimming for fitness classes. This kind of option gives students who are not sports orientated the opportunity to experience success and apply their health-related skills.

Numerous examples of games and fun activities are available (Corbin, 1976; Dauer & Pangrazi, 1986) for use at primary level. These activities can also incorporate simple stunts and experiments, such as heart rate measurement, to introduce youngsters to fitness concepts.

2. The factual material that needs to be presented to students concerning cardiovascular health is fairly extensive, and on some occasions this may mean teaching in a classroom setting while on others the gymnasium or field might be appropriate. Whichever format is chosen, in order to maintain maximum interest and curiosity, the material should be directed closely to students as individuals, their friends and

immediate family. Adolescents in particular are concerned with their personal physical development, regardless of their sports ability, and so the approach should always be 'student-centred' to achieve maximum effect. A variety of teaching methodologies, such as discussion, role play, experimentation, and use of audio-visual material, will help to stimulate interest.
3. If not used with understanding and sensitivity, fitness testing can defeat the object of maximum student involvement in cardiovascular activity. The purpose of fitness testing is to provide an initial baseline measure of fitness for students followed by regular monitoring for signs of improvement or decline. Unfortunately tests of cardiovascular fitness are more accurately measures of *performance*. Student scores on a 12-minute run will reflect hereditary differences in each student's physiological make-up, such as heart size and muscle fibre type. Only part of each student's score will reflect the degree of conditioning or training that we usually refer to when we use the term 'fitness'. The problem has already been alluded to (Williams, 1984). If lifetime fitness is the major concern, it makes little sense to continually compare our students to their peers. High cardiovascular performance is not possible for the majority because of genetic limitation, and comparison between our most athletic and least capable students is unsuitable. Some of us are blessed with high performance sports car engines which are capable of winning races. Most of us have to be content as family saloons. Both types of engines can provide a lifetime service if used regularly and kept in peak condition. The implication of this is that we should emphasise activity and improvement when dealing with cardiovascular fitness in the curriculum. The use of percentiles and norms of performance have limited value and may work to discourage those students who need the most encouragement.

To summarise, we have, through the physical education curriculum, the power to significantly enhance the long-term cardiovascular health and well-being of our students. If we provide accurate information and allow our students to understand the mechanisms involved in cardiovascular fitness, they are more likely to make intelligent decisions. If we help students to learn the skills of fitness and provide opportunities to enjoy a variety of activities which will promote cardiovascular fitness, we will go a long way to achieving our goal.

References

AAHPERD (1985) *Health-related physical fitness test manual.* Reston, Virginia: American Alliance for Health, Physical Education, Recreation and Dance.
ALMOND, L. (1983) Health-related fitness. *British Journal of*

Physical Education. Vol. 14 (2).

BASSEY, E. J. & FENTEM, P. H. (1981). *Exercise: the facts.* Oxford: Oxford University Press.

CORBIN, C. B. (1976). *Becoming physically educated in the elementary school.* (Second edition). Philadelphia: Lea and Febiger.

CORBIN, C. B., & LINDSEY, R. (1985) *Concepts of Physical Fitness.* (Fifth edition). Dubuque, Iowa: Wm. Brown Co. (formerly Concepts in Physical Education).

CORBIN, C. B., & LINDSEY, R. (1982) *Fitness for life.* London: Gage Publ.

CUNDIFF, D. E. (Ed.) (1985). *Implementation of health fitness exercise programmes.* Reston, Virginia: American Alliance for Health, Physical Education, Recreation and Dance.

DAUER, V. P. & PANGRAZI, R. P. (1986). *Dynamic physical education for elementary school children.* (Eighth edition), Minneapolis, MS: Burgess Publ.

KUNTZLEMAN, C. (October, 1984). Do your kids feel this good? *Prevention.*

PAFFENBARGER, R. S. et al. (1984). A natural history of athleticism and cardiovascular health. *Journal of the American Medical Association.* Vol. 252 .

POLLOCK, M. L. (1978). How much exercise is enough? *Physician and Sportsmedicine.* Vol. 6 .

SLAVA, S., LAURIE, D. R. & CORBIN, C. B. (1984). Long-term effects of a conceptual physical education programme. *Research Quarterly for Exercise and Sport.* Vol. 55

WILLIAMS, D. (1984). The educational implications of the submaximal oxygen uptake test. *British Journal of Physical Education.* Vol. 15 (3).

This chapter first appeared in the *British Journal of Physical Education,* 1985, Vol. 16 (3) .

Chapter Five

Muscle Fitness

**Jim Whitehead
and Charles Corbin**

Figure 1. Muscle fitness for the abdominals: sit-ups.

Readers of earlier chapters will be familiar with the ongoing theme of 'lifetime fitness.' This concept is fundamental to the philosophy of the authors, who believe that a major objective of school physical education should be to equip all pupils with the values, knowledge and skills that will enable them to solve their own physical fitness problems and plan their own exercise regimens.

The previous chapter explained why cardiovascular fitness is the foundation of health-related fitness. This chapter will deal with what is broadly termed here 'muscle fitness'—or more specifically, strength and muscular endurance. It will state *why* it should be an important part of the programme, *what* students need to know, and *how* to implement the principles into practice.

Why teach concepts of muscle fitness?

Nearly everybody understands that strength is the ability of muscles to exert force, and most people similarly know that muscular endurance refers to the capacity of muscles to go on working against resistance. Unfortunately, many do not understand the values of these aspects of health-related fitness to their well being, and furthermore, there are many myths which exist regarding muscle fitness. For example, some shy away from strength training for fear of becoming 'muscle bound.' Others still believe that muscle fitness training is not appropriate, even detrimental, to participation in certain sports.

The origins of this detractive mythology are something of a mystery. Perhaps the roots lie in the old music hall or circus strongman acts. It may be that the term 'overload' elicits connotations of overstrain, and the concept 'progressive resistance' is subconsciously read as progressively excrutiating. Whatever the reasons, it is a sad fact that many in Britain have an emotive reaction to 'strength' or 'muscle,' and often visualize a red-faced competitor in the World's Strongest Man event on television. This is a situation that only education can remedy.

Consider the facts: problems related to poor muscle fitness are widespread. The majority of cases of low back pain are related to muscle weakness or inflexibility. A recent estimate suggests that back problems cost Britain £500 million a year (H.M.S.O., 1985). The size of this problem is probably best not imagined in money anyway. In real terms, it means widespread human pain and disability. In the USA, medical reports indicate that approximately 80% of the population suffer from low back pain at some time in their lives, and it is suspected that the figures are similar for the UK.

Low back pain is not the only problem associated with poor muscle fitness. Weak

muscles do not guarantee the integrity of the joints which they cross. The result is a greater susceptibility to strains and sprains and a greater predisposition to postural problems. In addition, poor muscle fitness limits physical activity performance—including skill performance—and thus restricts recreational fun. (Consider, for example, the weak child with heavy tennis racquet.) Not surprisingly, there are sociological and psychological consequences of poor muscle fitness as well. Over twenty years ago, researchers (e.g. Clarke & Clarke, 1961) found that stronger children had higher social status with their peers, and more recently, other researchers (e.g. Tucker, 1983a, 1983b) have shown that strength relates positively to self-esteem.

Fortunately, the good news is that most of these problems are preventable, or can be alleviated relatively easily. It is almost a quarter of a century (1961) since Hans Kraus coined the term 'Hypokinetic Disease,' meaning diseases caused or related to lack of physical activity. Even if many physical educators are not presently familiar with the book (also titled *Hypokinetic Disease),* or the term, they will most likely remember the Kraus-Weber Tests of Minimum Muscular Fitness. Kraus administered this six-item muscle test to several thousand low back pain sufferers attending a treatment clinic and found that most failed, but with exercise therapy, test scores improved and back problems diminished. However, in the long term follow-up, the patients who stopped exercising again failed the tests as their back problems reappeared, emphasising that health-related fitness is a state of being—it cannot be stored or saved.

Simple logic demonstrates that individuals with good muscular fitness will manage manual work more easily and are likely to find more fun and satisfaction from sports participation. Skill learning and performance will be easier and the onset of fatigue is delayed. Increased and more

enthusiastic sports and games participation also has other fitness benefits. Continuous muscle fitness exercise of the appropriate type can improve cardiovascular fitness and tension release is facilitated (see chapter 9). Finally, but not lastly in importance for many participants, physical activity for muscular fitness helps you look good. Indeed, a good figure or physique seems to be desirable, and its acquisition is one important motivation behind the current fitness boom.

Associated with looking good is the concept of a suitable balance between body fatness and muscle mass. It has been consistently shown that obese children and adults who have attempted low calorie diets over many years have experienced reduced muscle mass. Their muscles are often weak and small. Muscle tissue is the agent which burns calories and for this reason reduced muscle tissue will result in fewer calories burnt even at rest—a lower BMR (basal metabolic rate). Obesity can be avoided or treated by maintaining an active and healthy muscle mass by increasing BMR. This can be achieved by simple daily muscular exercise.

What students need to know about muscular fitness

Knowledge and Understanding

The facts about muscular fitness that have already been stated will obviously affect our student's attitudes and enhance their capacities for intelligent decision-making. The knowledge of students must, of course, be considerably expanded. An understanding of the effects of the different exercise types and programmes is central to involvement. Ideally, methods of improving muscle fitness, ranging from free weights and resistance machines to the various calisthenic regimens, should be taught, and preferably knowledge of these methods will be acquired through experiential learning.

Knowing that exercise such as weight training, and other forms of muscle fitness training, are good for you is not enough. Some cognitive skills are also necessary to reach the top of the stairway to fitness (see chapter 1) and to become a capable physical fitness problem solver. Perhaps the first of these cognitive skills to be considered when dealing with muscular fitness, could be loosely termed 'consumer skills.' Earlier, the mythology surrounding the concept of 'muscle' was mentioned, and the experience of the authors is that popular (mis)conceptions can be a powerful influence on would-be exercise 'consumers.' We advocate that several topics should be thoroughly explained.

The first of these concerns safety—particularly in relation to weight training, as there seems to be a common belief that using free weights is a dangerous activity. This is not so, although any activity involving apparatus and movement does have an inherent risk. As long as supervision and teaching are sensible, the risks are negligible (Whitehead & Biddle, 1981) and usually far less than for other activities and sports.

A second myth centres around the idea that strength training will make a person 'muscle bound.' The suggestion is that muscle fitness training reduces flexibility and range of joint movement as a result of over-developed muscles. Evidence indicates that with a proper training programme, including appropriate stretching exercises, muscle boundness need not occur. In fact, properly trained athletes who use strength training are often more flexible than athletes in sports not using strength training.

Another common myth is that women will develop bulging muscles from muscle fitness training. In fact, it is almost impossible for females to develop bulging muscles because of their low levels of testosterone. What *is* a likely outcome is an improvement in muscle shape and tone—the prime requisite for a trim, athletic figure. However, it should be noted that strength training does build muscle. This muscle can help females look better and enhance performance. This is especially true for those with mesomorphic body types.

The final myths are that strength training slows you down, and muscles turn to fat in later years. Many famous athletes can be cited (e.g., Coe, Mennea) to disprove the former, and the latter is physiologically impossible. If muscular people do get fat, then an examination of their calorie intake and expenditure might better explain the obesity.

In addition to presenting information to dispelling myths about muscular strength there are many other important topics deserving of coverage. Some of these are listed below.

- Types of muscle fitness exercise including isometrics, isotonics, isokinetics and plyometrics
- Types of muscle contractions: concentric vs. eccentric
- Functions of muscles: agonists vs. antagonists
- Threshold and target zones for building muscular strength: low reps with high resistance
- Threshold and target zones for building

muscular endurance: high reps with low resistance
- Muscle fitness terminology, including the meaning of an exercise SET, repetitions (REPS), and PRE (Progressive Resistance Exercise)

Self-Testing and Self-Monitoring
The ability to *test* one's own muscle fitness as an ongoing diagnostic aid to exercise planning is another necessary skill. Fortunately this can be done easily, and with a minimum of apparatus. It is important that students understand how to do the many self-tests correctly, and which muscle groups are involved. Children often find this difficult, and sometimes even coaches and teachers lack a clear knowledge of muscle action in basic exercises. The classic example of this point is the sit-up (figure 1), where many instructors do not understand the action of the hip flexors (psoas), and still use straight-legged sit-ups as an (ostensible) abdominal muscle test. There are many good tests available (e.g. Corbin & Lindsey, 1985; Getchell, 1983; Heyward, 1984) where these exercises are clearly explained, and reference to them is recommended.

The self-evaluation of muscle fitness can be done isometrically using dynamometers or other devices such as tensiometers. Isotonic strength testing can be done with free weights, weight machines or isotonic calisthenics such as press-ups or sit-ups. Common sense is a reasonable guide to assessing muscle fitness levels from test results—the ability to handle body weight, as with isotonic calisthenics, is one obvious criterion. There are some sex-related performance differences to be aware of, particularly where arm and shoulder strength are concerned. The wide variation in individual abilities will mean that both sexes will need modification of some muscle tests anyway. Press-ups with knees on the floor, and bent-arm hang as a substitute for chins, are good examples of such modifactions. Several texts (e.g. AAPHERD, 1985, Corbin & Lindsey, 1982; 1985) contain scoring criteria for fitness evaluation and, again, these are recommended.

Exercise Prescription Skills
When these latter skills are mastered, the individual is capable of self-evaluation and diagnosis of personal muscle fitness needs. The final and most important skill is the *prescription and implementation* of an exercise programme. The first step is to choose the most appropriate activity, and here, knowledge, personal experience, and personal preference all play a part. Thus, two individuals both wanting an emphasis on high repetition, low resistance work for a muscular endurance effect, might self-prescribe different activities. One might begin with popmobility, whilst the other tries circuit weight training. Both can achieve the same results.

Actually planning the programme of exercise requires an intelligent understanding of several basic fitness concepts. The principles of specificity, overload, and progression are basic to exercise prescription, as is the F.I.T. principle (Frequency, Intensity, Time; see previous chapter). The desirability of avoiding muscle soreness in novices or exercise 'returnees' is important as is the provision for variety. In fact, the complexities of planning nicely illustrates the difference between fitness as something we *do to* people, and fitness as something people can *do for themselves*. The following section should help provide a basis for programme planning.

How might the principles and philosophy be put into practice?
There is no 'best' programme for teaching muscular fitness concepts, and it is obvious that many factors have to be considered in each particular situation where a teaching strategy is being designed. There are, however, several

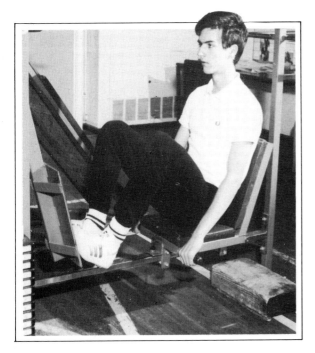

philosophical constructs and several general principles which largely form the foundation of good practice.

A vital aspect is the general *philosophy* that advocates lifetime physical fitness. Central to this philosophy is the belief that physical activity is good for you, and that we are providing an essential service for our student 'clients' based on their present and future needs. From this basic philosophy should stem a congruent *style* of practical application.

There can be many facets to this teaching style. Hopefully, teachers who believe in lifetime fitness will try to be good models and project an enthusiastic image. Recognizing that knowledge is vital to intelligent decision-making, the explanation of the health-related outcomes of all physical acitivity is desirable. Thus, for example, the muscular endurance benefits of swimming could be outlined and reinforced during a skill learning stroke session.

Vital to this philosophy is a style of teaching which is sympathetic to the feelings of all children. Sometimes, in the hustle and bustle of daily class management, it is difficult not to resort to an all-action, no-nonsense style, which to many shy or less able students, can appear insensitive or intimidating. Consideration of this problem is perhaps most important when muscle fitness assessment and evaluation is being conducted. Health-related fitness testing is a personal matter and should not become a competition between students. With a carefully engineered strategy of reinforcing effort over performance, an empathetic class atmosphere of support can be cultivated, which will be particularly productive and rewarding for those who need help the most—the less able. Even so, there may still be some students who will not wish to be evaluated in public at all, and their feelings and rights should be respected. Some may need special attention, and this will be discussed later.

Finally, regarding teaching style and philosophy, a major concern of the authors must be mentioned. If we believe that physical activity is beneficial to our health and well being (and also fun), then it is totally illogical to present it as otherwise by using exercise as a punishment. A press-up is a valuable exercise for promoting muscular fitness of the triceps, pectoralis and anterior deltoids, so why prescribe it, or sit-ups (or running laps), as a painful, negative reinforcement? It would seem far more sensible to try to facilitate intrinsic motivation by promoting the personal benefits of participation, and positively reinforcing this with praise for effort (see Biddle, 1984, for a full discussion of these issues.)

Another important factor in programme design is the physical and psychological developmental level of student. Primary school children are obviously not physically mature enough for high intensity, low repetition strength work. Such activity is usually left until students are physically advanced enough to handle it, particularly when loading on the spine is considered. The British Amateur Weightlifters' Association (B.A.W.L.A.) does not sanction competition in *weightlifting* until the age of thirteen and they also stress caution with late physical maturers. However sensible, low intensity *weight training* is perfectly acceptable for most secondary age students, and there are many reasons to recommend it. Teachers who wish for more information on this topic, or who would like to take a teacher's course, are recommended to contact the B.A.W.L.A.

Psychologically, young children are not ready for high intensity work either. Their attention span is shorter, and long term goals have less significance to them. Similarly, with concepts of health, young children show little concern for the future and are more interested in the present. The more immediate effects of muscle fitness work on their bodily appearance and physical performance are thus the more suitable aspects to emphasise. As the students reach and complete adolescence in the final years of their compulsory education, they become far more receptive to lifetime fitness concepts, and have greater ability to use abstract thinking for problem solving, and the emphasis can therefore change to future considerations.

In practical terms, these developmental differences indicate short intervals of muscle fitness work and concepts (for example, during warm-ups) as part of a varied and enjoyable curriculum of sport, games and activities for younger pupils, with progression to more formally blocked sessions of muscle fitness work (such as circuit training or weight training) as the students mature. These longer blocks should, of course, be educational, with the emphasis on learning to exercise and the acquisition of knowledge and lifetime cognitive skills. Fortunately, the clear cut nature of most muscle fitness exercises makes the giving of information easy during teaching (e.g., "This is an exercise for the muscles at the front of the thigh ...", etc.). The problem solving skills follow naturally from this knowledge (e.g., "Which exercises do you think a freestyle

swimmer might best use in a programme?") and can help to make the learning of anatomy and muscle function an interesting topic.

Extra curricular provision of health-related fitness activities can be a valuable adjunct to regular teaching, and constitutes a concrete demonstration of the lifetime fitness philosophy in action. Such provision widens extra curricular opportunity to all students rather than just the few elite games players who have traditionally been catered for. Interestingly though, a 'fringe benefit' in the form of sports opportunity can arise from participation and progression from one muscle fitness activity – weight training. Several secondary schools have found weightlifting a literally golden opportunity to compete because of the bodyweight divisions in the sport. Of course, this possibility should not pervert the reasons for providing weight training, and the majority of participants will

not become competitors, but will simply enjoy the activity and value its fitness benefits.

Finally in this section on principles into pratice is a discussion of muscle fitness work as a *remedial* activity for less able students. There are many advantages in using this aspect of health-related fitness as a basis of the provision for those with such exceptional needs. A primary advantage is the motivation which results from improvement in performance. Muscle fitness improves very quickly with correct exercise, particularly when fitness levels are low to begin with, and, moreover, it is easily measurable in increased repetitions or resistance. This fast return for effort can be a revelation to students who may have previously written themselves off as physically incompetent.

The lack of potential embarrassment to sometimes reluctant exercisers is another valuable aspect that can be capitalized on. Most muscle fitness improving activities require little skill so good style can be quickly and confidently attained. This particularly applies to weight training, where the exercises can easily be performed 'correctly,' even though the repetitions may be fewer, or the resistance lower than for the other students. Also, whatever the muscle fitness activity, a bonus to many sensitive improvers is that no body-revealing uniforms are required. Loose-fitting, problem-camouflaging sweat-shirts are quite acceptable and help furnish the desired 'exerciser' image.

Attraction to muscle fitness activities may also be enhanced because they are invariably conducted indoors, and under the close control of a teacher. Not only is comfort facilitated (an important consideration in the British climate), but the atmosphere engendered by a sympathetic teacher is unlikely to threaten those students who are sensitive to peer group performance-level pressures. Fortunately, most muscle fitness improvement activities are

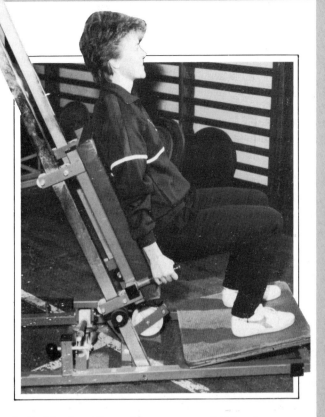

individual, with no team responsibilities to uphold, so this is rarely a problem. In fact, it is the authors' experience that the strength and muscular endurance of low ability students quickly improves through training to a level that gains the respect of other pupils. Also, this greater muscle fitness aids the performance of other physical activities, giving an additional boost to confidence and motivation that can be most gratifying to the student. Seeing those with exceptional needs helped on the road to lifetime fitness also brings rewards to the teacher—a job satisfaction that is highly fulfilling to those who are committed to a physical education for ALL philosophy.

In conclusion, it can be stated that muscle fitness is an important but often neglected aspect of health-related fitness. Good teaching, applied in a style congruent with a lifetime fitness philosophy, will provide students with the knowledge, cognitive skills, and practical experience necessary for intelligent decision-making regarding personal muscle fitness needs and exercise programme planning. Younger pupils should have muscle fitness activities and concepts introduced at frequent short intervals during a general programme of physical activity, games and sports. Longer blocks of formal teaching, with a greater emphasis on cognitive skills, can be organized for older students. Because of the potential, muscle fitness activities are particularly indicated for remedial work with less able students.

The purpose of this chapter has been to outline a rationale for the inclusion of muscle fitness concepts in the curriculum. By exposing our youth to the health demands of lifetime muscular fitness and also giving them the opportunity to take part in a whole range of activities that promote muscle fitness, we give them the educational privilege of *CHOICE*.

Students will leave school with the skills and knowledge to safely develop muscle fitness for sports, or a minority may wish to develop muscle fitness *as* a sport. It is hoped that the majority will choose to incorporate some form of regular muscular conditioning in their lifestyle, whether it be weight training at the local health spa or gym, dance aerobics, or simply performing minimum muscular fitness activities at home for health on a daily basis.

Readers requiring further information are encouraged to read the many texts available— some of which have been recommended in this book.

References
AAHPERD (1985). *Health-related physical fitness test manual*. Reston, VA: AAHPERD.
BIDDLE, S. J. H. (1984). Motivational issues in health-related fitness: a note of caution. *British Journal of Physical Education*, Vol. 15 (1)
CLARKE, H. H. & CLARKE, D. H. (1961). Social status and mental health of boys as related to their maturity, structural, and strength characteristics. *Research Quarterly*, Vol. 32 (3)
CORBIN, C. B. & LINDSEY, R. (1985). *Concepts of Physical Fitness*. Dubuque, Iowa: Wm. Brown Co. (Formerly *Concepts of Physical Education*).
CORBIN, C. B. & LINDSEY, R. (1982). *Fitness for Life*. London: Gage Publ.
FALLS, H. R. (1980). Modern concepts of physical fitness. *Journal of Physical Education and Recreation*, Vol. 4.
GETCHELL, B. (1983). *Physical fitness: A way of life*. New York, John Wiley & Sons.

HEYWARD, V. H. (1984). *Designs for fitness*. Minneapolis: Burgess Publishing Company.
H.M.S.O. (1985). *Social Trends*. London Central Statistical Office.
KRAUS, H. & HIRSCHLAND, R. P. (1954). Minimum muscular fitness tests in school children. *Research Quarterly*, Vol. 25 (2).
KRAUS, H. & RAUB, W. (1961). *Hypokinetic disease*. Springfield: Charles C. Thomas.
LEAR, P. J. (1985). *Know the Game: Weight training*. London: A & C. Black.
TUCKER, L. A. (1983a). Muscular strength and mental health. *Journal of Personality and Social Psychology*, Vol. 45 (6)
TUCKER, L. A. (1986). Weight training: A tool for the improvement of self and body concepts of males. *Journal of Human Movement Studies*, Vol. 9.
WHITEHEAD, J. R. & BIDDLE, S. J. H. (1981). Slimline Weightlifting. *British Journal of Physical Education*, Vol. 12 (3)

For information on B.A.W.L.A. school teacher courses, write to John Lear, B.A.W.L.A. Director of Coaching, 'The Willows,' 4 Fords Heath, Shrewsbury, Shropshire.

Credit is extended to Ken Fox who made valuable editorial comments to the authors during the preparation of this chapter.

This chapter first appeared in the *British Journal of Physical Education*, 1985, Vol. 16 (5).

Chapter Six

Flexibility; The Forgotten Part of Fitness

Charles Corbin and Ken Fox

Because of the high death and disease rate associated with various forms of heart disease, the importance of cardiovascular fitness to good health is well known to most people (see chapter 4). Primarily because coaches have realized the importance of strength and muscular endurance to success in sports and athletics, muscle fitness (see chapter 5) is also something that many athletes have come to value. In addition, the importance of muscle fitness for an athletic physique or a trim figure has been realized by an increasing number of people. Flexibility, also a component of health-related physical fitness, does not often receive the attention that is enjoyed by the other fitness parts. Perhaps this is because few people die from poor posture or back pain. Perhaps it is because many people do not realize that good flexibility can benefit health in many ways.

Traditionally stretching and flexibility have been regarded as the exclusive domain of the dancer or gymnast. Fortunately the trend towards activities such as dance aerobics, which incorporate stretching exercises into fitness sessions, are helping to emphasise the role of flexibility in total fitness development. Sadly, even though the best male gymnasts and dancers exhibit extremely high levels of strength *and* flexibility, the art of stretching is often regarded by males as unimportant or as something that "females do". Maybe the lesser interest in flexibility is because people believe that it is something that you are born with rather than something which can be developed with regular exercise, or perhaps the lack of attention results from the fact that many people simply do not know what flexibility is and why it is important. Whatever the reason, there is now ample evidence to suggest that educating people about flexibility is important to a total understanding of physical fitness.

What is flexibility?

Technically, flexibility is defined as "the range

of movement in a joint or group of joints" (Corbin and Lindsey, 1985). Each joint has it own range of motion depending on its type. For example, the knee flexes and extends but is not designed to rotate. The shoulder, however, does allow for rotation as a part of its normal range of motion. The muscles, ligaments, tendons, and bones which comprise and surround the joint all contribute to flexibility. Because shortness of muscles limits range of joint movement, and because increased length of muscle resulting from the right kind of regular exercise provides for optimal range of movement, we often equate flexibility with muscle length. For the remainder of this chapter we will consider flexibility to be sufficient muscle length to allow optimal range of movement in the joints.

At this point, another definition seems in order. While flexibility is a term used to describe one component of health-related physical fitness, stretching is the term used to describe the technique most often used to lengthen muscles and improve flexibility. For this reason, when we refer to stretching we mean exercises designed to build flexibility by putting the muscle into stretch beyond its normal length.

Why teach flexibility concepts?

The first real interest in flexibility as an ingredient of good health developed after World War II when physicians and physiotherapists came to realize the importance of developing long muscles as part of the treatment programmes for large numbers of orthopedic problems experienced by war veterans (Corbin, 1984). Subsequently studies of people with back problems (Kraus and Hirschland, 1954) illustrated the importance of flexibility in the prevention and treatment of such problems.

We now know that good flexibility is associated with prevention of back pain and the maintenance of good posture. For example, if the hamstring muscles (muscles of the back of the upper leg) are too short, leg pain can result as well as referred pain in the lower back. If the iliopsoas muscles (the hip flexors) are too short it can cause the pelvis to tip forward resulting in low back sway or lordosis. Lordosis is associated with low back pain. Lack of muscle length in other areas of the body can result in pain as well. There is now evidence to indicate that dysmenorohea, or painful menstruation, can, in some cases, be reduced or relieved by regular flexibility exercises.

Not to be overlooked is the importance of good flexibility to performance in sports and other types of physical activity. While the evidence is not overwhelming regarding the importance of flexibility to all performance, we do not need statistics to tell us that quality performances in activities such as dance, gymnastics, skating and diving require considerable flexibility. Likewise, a lunge in fencing or an overhead in badminton cannot be performed successfully by a person with limited flexibility. As early as the 1930's evidence began to accumulate supporting the contention that

shoulder and ankle flexibility were important to swimming performance. Current evidence shows no major advantage for elite distance runners with exceptional flexibility though we do know that lack of flexibility can cause problems for the recreational jogger.

The most recent evidence suggests that different types of athletes possess differing amounts of flexibility. What we don't know is whether these athletes chose their sports because they already possessed flexibility or whether participation in the sport is responsible for developing flexibility. Studies do show baseball players and athletics participants to be above average in flexibility of some areas of the body while basketball and soccer players show poor flexibility. Athletes involved in these sports perform sprints requiring leg movement through a limited range. If stretching exercises are not frequently used a short range of muscle action results. For example, athletes in these sports are notorious for their lack of hamstring flexibility. Weight trainers who train properly by exercising through the full range of joint motion have above normal flexibility, thus suggesting that the notion that strength training results in "muscleboundness" is a myth. As you might expect gymnasts and swimmers excel in flexibility, but quite unexpectedly wrestlers do not.

It is our belief that a certain amount of "threshold" level of flexibility is necessary for most sports. The threshold is probably quite specific to each sport. Once the threshold has been reached, additional flexibility probably does not improve performance. Problems arise when performers lack critical threshold amounts. This is probably more likely to occur among recreational athletes than elite athletes who train on a regular schedule. It should be pointed out that many jobs and daily activities probably require threshold amounts of flexibility. Whereas some people may require less flexibility to perform recreational and daily

activities than others, all people need minimal amounts of flexibility to prevent muscle pain, soreness, and injury.

Not to be overlooked is the need for flexibility to prevent muscle, joint, and connective tissue injuries. Again the research evidence is not overwhelming, but there is indirect evidence that supports the need for flexibility in preventing injuries. Beginning joggers and skiers have many more injuries than more experienced athletes. The majority of these injuries are sprains and strains which very likely result when too short muscles are vigorously overstretched. Conventional wisdom suggests that long muscles, particularly in the ankles, legs, arms, shoulders, and trunk, will result in fewer injuries, particularly in contact and collision sports and in jobs which require vigorous bouncing stretch of the muscles.

What do students need to know about flexibility?

As children pass through their school years, they should acquire both *knowledge* and *skills* regarding flexibility.

Knowledge and Understanding

In addition to knowing what flexibility is and how it can benefit a person, there are other key concepts which are of importance to learners. Space does not allow a complete discussion of all the concepts but some of the more important

ones are dealt with here. The reader is directed to the references at the end of the chapter for more information concerning flexibility concepts.

Perhaps more than any other component of health-related fitness, flexibility is specific Students must learn that building flexibility in one muscle group does not result in flexibility in another muscle group. Further, many types of aerobic and sports activities may do little to build flexibility. To a large extent a person must do specific stretching exercises for a specific muscle group if flexibility is to be developed. In fact, as explained earlier, joggers, cricket, soccer and basketball players may actually *reduce* flexibility in certain body areas through regular participation because of the limited range of motion of the typical movement patterns of these sports.

It is true that long muscles and freedom of joint movement are desirable. However, learners need to understand that there is such a thing as too much range of joint movement. This is commonly called 'joint looseness.' There is evidence that an excessively loose joint, such as the knee, is especially susceptible to injury. Studies of American football players show that the risk of knee injury is 20 times as great among those with loose knees as those with "tight" knees. Because joint looseness can be a problem, exercises which overstretch the connective tissues of critical joints should be avoided. For example, the deep knee bend or full squat, the duck walk, crab football, and other similar exercises are not recommended. There are methods of testing looseness (Godshall, 1975; Nicholas, 1970). For those diagnosed to have loose joints, overload training to build muscles to support the effected joint is recommended. Special weight training exercises, or even bicycle riding which keeps the knee "in line", will build muscle fitness of the knee and help reduce joint looseness.

Just as exercises which can contribute to joint looseness should be avoided, so should certain stretching exercises which causes excessive pressure or mechanical disadvantages to the joints. Such exercises are considered to be "contraindicated exercises". Contraindicated exercises should be avoided by people who are considered at high risk, for example those who already have symptoms of back pain. Some exercises, such as the deep knee bend, as already discussed, are to be avoided by all people. Students should be aware of which exercises are contraindicated, including excessive back arching exercises, those causing pressure on the neck and knee, and those causing mechanical disadvantage to the low back. A more complete discussion of these exercises and acceptable substitutes are documented in other sources (Corbin and Lindsey, 1985).

In a previous section we discussed the value of flexibility in preventing injury and pain, and improving performance. Over the long term stretching exercises build flexibility and the benefits of good fitness become apparent. But what of the "short term" benefits of stretching? In the short term stretching is valuable as a "warm up" which may help reduce the risk of injuries in subsequent performance. It is effective as a technique for bringing immediate relief of muscle cramps and if done right after exercise it may help relieve muscle soreness.

Unfortunately, many of our students are not

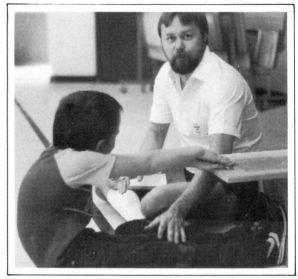

Figure 1. The sit and reach test: A test of low back and hamstring flexibility.

aware of the need for a warm up. Many, if not most of them, do not realize that stretching a muscle prior to use will lengthen it and allow a greater range of joint movement. It is known, for example, that you can perform better on a sit and reach test if you have performed several sit and reach movements prior to recording a measurement. It is very important that we teach our students a good set of exercises which can be used as a warm up. These exercises can be performed before sports activities and before fitness tests. We recommend a static stretching warm up.

We also need to be more careful in teaching about the warm up not to lead students astray. Almost all experts agree that a stretching warm up should precede regular vigorous activity, but students must understand that a warm up is no substitute for a regular flexibility programme. Some people think that a stretching warm up will protect them from injury even if they have been inactive and lack good flexibility. In fact, a warm up is better than nothing for a person who attempts to perform vigorous exercise after a long period of inactivity, but the warm up without regular flexibility training will be of limited value. Short muscles do not become long overnight or with a few minutes of stretching. Students must realise that daily flexibility training is the only way to develop good flexibility. Of course a regular stretching warm up can be a significant part of a regular daily flexibility programme and should be recommended prior to vigorous activity.

Another benefit of regular stretching is its value in relieving muscle soreness, including muscle cramps. The work of de Vries (1980), in which he used electromyography, documented the importance of static stretch in reducing muscle activity. We now know that to relieve a muscle cramp a muscle should be put in stretch and held there until the cramp subsides. This same stretch is thought to relieve delayed localised muscle soreness by breaking what is referred to as the 'muscle spasm cycle'. While there is some debate as to the exact causes of different types of delayed localised muscle soreness, most experts feel that static stretching immediately after vigorous exercise and static stretching of the muscles experiencing soreness, even the day after exercise, can be beneficial in reducing soreness. Thus a stretching *cool down* may be important in addition to a stretching warm up. It should be noted that soreness resulting from injury is not the same as soreness resulting from regular vigorous exercise. An injured muscle should not be overstretched until it is healed and care should be taken to be aware of the cause of muscle soreness before muscle stretching is applied.

Self-testing and self-monitoring skills

As with all parts of health-related fitness, students should learn to assess their own flexibility. Self-testing provides them with information which can be used in planning a total fitness programme, including a programme of flexibility development. Rather than the teacher testing students, it is recommended that the teacher teach students how to test themselves. In this way self-testing can be used to monitor fitness for a lifetime. It is recommended that students keep records of their own self-tests administered regularly over

a period of time. This will allow them to determine improvement resulting from their personal programmes of exercise.

Because flexibility is highly specific, there is no single self-test which can be used to evaluate flexibility. In fact many self-tests will be necessary if comprehensive testing of flexibility is desired. There are many good references which describe a wide variety of flexibility self-tests (Corbin, 1984; Corbin and Lindsey, 1983; Corbin and Lindsey, 1985) and the reader is referred to these for complete details. We would, however, like to comment further on a few tests and testing techniques.

There are many devices for measuring flexibility, including goniometers for measuring angles, fleximeters for measuring degree of bending, and anthrometers or anthropometers for measuring joints. More sophisticated devices include electrogoniometers, photogoniometers, and radiogoniometers, which are all quite recent in their development. Of course these devices cost money and would be of little value to the average person for self-assessment at home. Fortunately, many tests can be done in the home with a minimum of equipment and a minimum of training.

The most widely used self-test is the sit and reach test (see Figure 1). It is quite good for home self-assessment because it requires only a ruler or measuring stick and a box or small chair and because it measures muscle length of both the back and leg muscles. Since these are the muscle groups in which the average person is likely to experience pain and which are most often used in work and recreational activities, this test has relevance to most people. Also standards of performance are available for people of most age groups on this test (AAHPERD, 1985); Corbin & Lindsey, 1985). To do the test the measuring stick is fixed with tape to a box with the stick's end overlapping. After a warm up, the person reaches as far as possible recording the distance reached along the stick. The knees are kept straight and the two hands overlapped. Other commonly used tests which are easy to use in the home include the arm and shoulder reach, the prone trunk lift, and various tests for assessing the length of the different muscle groups of the legs. None requires a significant amount of equipment.

Exercise prescription skills

After the student has learned the facts about flexibility and has done some self-testing to determine his or her current level of flexibility, a programme of flexibility can be planned. Flexibility can be developed using several different methods. Each student will have to decide which type of stretching is best for himself or herself.

For most people static stretching exercises are recommended. Though passive stretching is often used as synonomous, static stretching is now considered the preferred term. Static stretching means stretching the muscle slowly beyond its normal length and holding the extended length for several seconds. Static stretch can be done with the aid of gravity, as in a standing toe touch, with the assist of the antagonist muscles, as in the sitting toe touch when you use the muscles on the front of the legs to help you reach your toes, or with the assist from a partner, as in the sitting toe touch when a partner gently pushes on your back as you try to touch your toes. Any of these types of static stretch can be effective if the muscle is stretched beyond its normal length, though some experts prefer a combination of an antagonist contraction and a passive assist. The antagonist stretch tends to relax the muscle to be stretched because of reciprocal innervation and the assist will allow more stretch than the antagonist muscles can produce by themselves.

Ballistic stretch is bouncing stretch or stretch caused by the momentum of a forceful movement or external force. It is sometimes called active stretch though the preferred term

is ballistic stretch. Ballistic stretch can be done using the force of body weight and gravity as in bobbing up and down while trying to reach toes in a toe touch. The antagonist muscle, or another person, can also assist in giving a ballistic stretch just as with static stretch. Although this method is not the best for use by most of our students it seems to have been traditionally the most often used in schools.

PNF (proprioceptive neuromuscular facilitation) is another type of stretching which has gained recent popularity. It is basically either static or ballistic stretch which is preceded by an isometric contraction of the muscle to be stretched. Some experts feel that the isometric contraction prior to stretching produces greater lengthening of the muscle. There are many variations of PNF, all of which seem to develop flexibility. However, there is no convincing evidence at this point to say that PNF is significantly better than other stretching techniques.

For beginning exercisers and those who do not plan to develop especially high levels of flexibility for sports performances, we recommend static stretch with antagonist muscle contraction and a partner assist. Because there is no bouncing against the muscle the stretch reflex is not activated. Also the reciprocal innervation resulting from the contraction of the antagonist muscle makes lengthening of the muscle easier. For these reasons delayed localised soreness and muscle injury is less likely. Static PNF is also a good choice. Ballistic stretch may be appropriate for high level athletes who will be doing high level performances requiring ballistic movement skills but we do not recommend it for most people. Even for athletes who have decided that ballistic stretching is a necessary part of their training programme, a static or PNF stretching warm up should *precede* the ballistic stretch.

Whichever technique is included for a person's exercise programme, the FIT principle

should be followed in doing the exercises (see chapter 4). The exercises should be done *Frequently* enough, *Intensely* enough, and for the correct amount of *Time*. Frequency for flexibility is a minimum of three days a week and optimally every day. Intensity for flexibility means stretching the muscle approximately 10% longer than normal (not to the point of pain but enough to feel the pull against the muscle). The length of time is 10 to 60 seconds for each static stretch. Of course the FIT formula must be applied in the form of separate exercises for each muscle group you want to stretch.

Some sources that include a wide variety of exercises are listed in the reference section. These sources can be made available to students so they can try the various exercises using the techniques already described. The book *Stretching* (Anderson, 1980) is the most popular current source and contains a wide variety of exercises for many different sports. It should be noted, however, that the book does include a number of exercises which are contraindicated for some people. In teaching students from any book contraindicated exercises should be clearly identified for students and the reasons why they are contraindicated should be discussed.

How can the programme best promote flexibility in students?

Motivating students to develop flexibility through stretching seems to be one of the more difficult tasks in the teaching of health-related physical fitness. Primary school students and many secondary students will probably not relate well to the concepts of back pain and disease because they may not have experienced them. They may not seem like real problems to them. The following advice is offered to make the task of the teacher easier.

1. Always use a warm up which incorporates static stretching exercises of the muscles to be used before the daily physical education activities. Explain clearly why each exercise was selected and which muscles it stretches. Emphasize good technique and explain the reasons why static stretching is preferred.

2. In class, try to relate flexibility to later life, a time when it will be a problem for many people, by encouraging students to give their parents, grandparents, and older brothers and sisters information about flexibility and the prevention of back pain, muscle soreness, and poor posture.

3. Use the many stunts and evaluation techniques available in the recommended texts to show students how flexibility can affect posture and how it is specific to each different joint and muscle group. For example, some students may do well on the sit-and-reach but not so well on the shoulder flexibility stunt. Use this to promote discussion and understanding.

4. Use role models, including yourself, in the demonstration of the importance of maintaining good flexibility. Show soccer

players, sprinters, gymnasts, dancers and other athletes doing flexibility exercises and discuss how it can help their performance and prevent injury.

5. Stretching can also be used as a way of practising muscle relaxation. Have students do cool down stretching after vigorous activity. Stretching can also be used as a technique for anxiety reduction during class or prior to competition.

6. Finally flexibility is part of fitness that can improve more quickly than some parts of fitness such as strength. Unfortunately those least likely to stretch are those who may need it the most. These students may say, "but I've *never* been able to do that" and believe that they are stuck with being inflexible for life. There is no doubt that it will be harder for some than others to develop good flexibility. But regular measurement and encouragement will show these students that improvements can be made. The ensuing confidence will increase their desire to make stretching a part of their daily activity.

Summary

To summarize, flexibility may often be forgotten by people who promote physical fitness. Nevertheless, it is a very important part of fitness. There are many ways to build it which can be learned by school-age children. With the proper understanding of the facts about flexibility, self-testing and self-monitoring skills, and exercise prescription skills students can learn to plan a flexibility programme which will become a central part of their total plan for developing fitness for a lifetime. The resultant lifetime benefits of decreased chance of soreness and injury, reduced risk of back pain and muscular tension, improved posture, and possibilities of improved work productivity and sports performance seem worth the few minutes of stretching required each day.

References

AMERICAN ALLIANCE FOR HEALTH, PHYSICAL EDUCATION, RECREATION AND DANCE (1985). *Health-related physical fitness test manual*. Reston, Virginia: AAHPERD.

ANDERSON, B. (1980). *Stretching*. London: Pelham.

BEAULIEU, J. E. (1980). *Stretching for all sports*. Pasedena, California: The Athletic Press.

CORBIN, C. B. (1984). Flexibility. In J.A. Nicholas & E.B. Hershman (Eds.) *Clinics in sports medicine*, Vol 3 (1). Philadelphia: W.B. Saunders.

CORBIN, C. B. & LINDSEY, R., (1983). *Fitness for life*. London: Gage Publishers.

CORBIN, C. B. & LINDSEY, R. (1985). *Concepts of physical fitness* (5th Ed.). Dubuque, Iowa: Wm. C. Brown.

CORBIN, C. B. & NOBLE, L. M., (1980). Flexibility: a major component of physical fitness. *JOPERD*, Vol. 51 June)

DeVRIES, H.A. (1980). *Physiology of Exercise*. Dubuque, Iowa: Wm. C. Brown.

GODSHALL, R. W. (1975). The prediction of athletic injury: an eight year study. *Journal of Sports Medicine*. Vol. 3.

KRAUS, H. and HIRSCHLAND, R. P. (1954). Minimum muscular fitness tests in school children, *Research Quarterly*, Vol. 25 (2).

NICOLAS, J. A. (1970). Injuries to the knee ligament. *Journal of the American Medical Association*, Vol. 212.

SHULTZ, P. (1979). Flexibility: day of the static stretch. *The Physician and Sports Medicine*, Vol. 7.

This chapter first appeared in the *British Journal of Physical Education*, 1985, Vol. 16 (6).

Chapter Seven

Body Composition: The Double-Edged Sword

Ken Fox & Charles Corbin

As with many aspects of the fitness market place, the world of weight control is plagued with gimmickry, fads, mythology, and ignorance. The commercial sector is never slow to take advantage and has firmly established the media image of slenderness. Diet books frequently head the best seller lists and magazines and weight loss pharmaceuticals and equipment are big business. In a world that is becoming more and more obsessed by body image, it is vital that physical educators 'clear the air' regarding body composition concepts and present students with accurate and unbiased facts about weight control. This chapter will deal with the concept of body composition as it applies to good health. The goal is to help physical educators prepare students to be discriminating and discerning fitness consumers.

Why should we be concerned about body composition?

The primary health problem (at least in the western world) relating to body composition concerns the carrying of *too much body fat*. Body fat is stored around the main organs in the body and within the muscles, but over half is stored in a layer just beneath the skin, making overfatness a visible phenomenon. In developed countries such as ours, where a sedentary lifestyle and rich, high-calorie diet is prevalent, a large percentage of both adults and children store too much of this fat, and many are overfat to the extent that they can be classed as obese. Figures are scarce for the British population, but in the USA at least one third of adults are overfat. The story for children is no less encouraging. Over 25% of school children are overfat, and the U.S. Department of Health and Human Services revealed that children on average have become fatter since the 1960s. Sadly, the longer a child remains obese through childhood, the greater the chance of becoming a fat adult, and *by the time adolescence is reached*

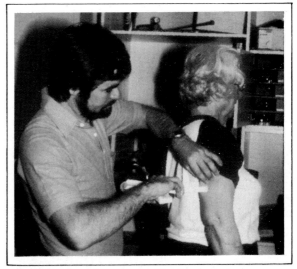

Figure 1: Measurement of body fat using skinfold calipers on the triceps skinfold.

there is an 80% chance that the fat child will remain fat rather than fit for life. Unfortunately, obesity, and to a lesser extent overfatness, is associated with serious organic impairments and a consequent shortened life. Overfat people have a higher risk of respiratory infections, high blood pressure, atherosclerosis, and have a higher prevalence of circulatory, respiratory and kidney problems. Diabetes, and bone and joint deterioration are also associated with being overfat. In addition, obese and overfat children and adults are likely to have poor self-esteem, suffer psychological maladjustments, and poor relationships with peers. Their condition usually results in an absence of vigorous physical activity, and resultant low scores in many aspects of physical fitness. Clearly, in both psychological and physiological health terms, it does not pay to carry too much body fat, and it should be a concern of health-related fitness programmes that students are aware of the process of personal body fat control.

Of equal importance is the problem of *too little body fat*, caused by excessive dieting, undereating, and hyperactivity. An extreme desire to be lean and thin can result in anorexia nervosa, bulimia, or to a less extreme extent, 'fear of obesity'. Anorexia, or self-induced starvation, is a disorder found almost exclusively among the teenage female population, and it has been estimated that one girl in every 100 may fall victim. Similarly, bulimia, or episodic binge eating and self-induced vomiting of food, is characteristic of the female population. Estimates of its prevalence among the American college-age females have ranged from 4% to 19%. 'Fear of obesity' is another recently recognised problem which is characteristic of achievement-orientated teenagers. Disorders such as these can eventually lead to serious ill-health, such as stunting of growth, delayed puberty, severe muscle wasting, and eventual death. Because of the dramatic increase in these conditions in recent decades, it is vital that education deals with the seriousness of eating disorders, and attempts to identify irregularities in their early stages.

A third problem concerning body composition is the case of the *undermuscled* individual. Often this condition is associated with the uncoordinated and/or obese child. It results from lack of activity in childhood to the extent that the child is so weak that he/she cannot manage his/her own body weight effectively. This severely handicaps the child in the sport setting and also in the daily routine of life. One of the best answers to this problem is to involve the child in a non-threatening exercise programme which includes regular weight training. The weak child with poor muscle development was discussed in chapter 5. Muscle underdevelopment and wasting, however, can also result from frequent reduced-calorie dieting and this problem will be dealt with here as it affects obesity and overfatness.

What should students learn about body composition?

With the health problems of body composition in mind, it is clear that all students should be aware of the facts and health risks associated with being overfat or underfat. They should be proficient in the skill of self-testing for body fatness, so that they can assess with reasonable accuracy whether or not they are experiencing problems. They should then be sufficiently expert to be able to recognise trends so that they can prescribe and carry out the right types of lifestyle changes that will necessitate a longterm solution to their difficulty. All in all, they should be in an independent position to accurately identify, and safely and effectively solve, their own body composition problems.

Defining the limits of overfatness and obesity is not easy. Researchers vary in their figures, and to complicate matters, levels are different for males and females after puberty. The inconsistencies in definition arise because the problems concerned with overfatness are identified by statistical associations and risks become greater as fatness increases. There is no clear-cut point at which obesity becomes dangerous to health, but there is a range where risks dramatically increase. For the sake of argument at this stage, overfatness can be described as having more than 19% for males, and 26% for females, of the total body weight as fat weight. Obesity begins around 25% for males and 32% for females. Underfatness is less easy to define. There is certainly a level of 'essential' fat that is required for maintenance of good health, but for males, this may be described as low as 3-4% body fat. Females who are not regularly involved in high levels of vigorous physical activity would not under normal circumstances have lower than 8-10% body fat. Female long distance runners, however, may have much lower levels. Concern should be shown and explanations sought if adolescent girls show levels as low as 10% body fat, especially if the trend has been steadily in a downward direction. Some attention needs to be given to body somatotype when interpreting body fat percentage figures.

There appears to be a wide range of body fatness which can be considered healthy. It makes little real sense to sub-categorise this range into poor, good, excellent, etc. because within this range, less body fat, is not necessarily better. Ideal levels depend on individual somatotype and how we feel about ourselves. We should be more concerned with monitoring individual trends over time in order to predict and prevent problems.

Measuring body fat percentage

In order to make decisions, students need to be able to monitor their body fat levels, so that they can determine their individual needs.

Traditionally, the *bathroom scale* has been the instrument used to measure fatness. Unfortunately, weighing scales inform us about changes in *body weight* but not *body composition*. If we thoroughly understand the concept of body composition and realise that changes in body weight can result from changes in body fluids, energy stores, muscle tissue gain or decrease, as well as fluctuations in body fat weight, it quickly becomes apparent that the weighing scales do not tell us all we need to know. As a result of an exercise programme, for instance, we may lose body fat because of the calorie deficit we have incurred, AND, at the same time, increase our muscle tissue weight because of the extra activity. The bathroom scales may show little change or even an INCREASE in body weight caused by the exercise programme, with the result that the exerciser gives up, feeling that the regime has failed. In fact, the exercise has caused a trimming down of the fat and an increase in muscle firmness, with a resultant firm and trim body. Weight then, does not tell us the whole story and the use of height/weight tables reflect this. Because muscle is denser than fat, it is possible for a heavily muscled person, such as a weightlifter, to be grossly overestimated by height/weight tables, even when he/she has a low body fat percentage. Conversely, an individual who has a very small and weak musculature, but who has a high level of body fat may register as normal on height/weight tables when realistically they are overfat. The use of height and weight criteria is even more confusing when dealing with children because of growth spurts and different rates of maturation. Remember, it is the fat weight, not the total body weight, that is associated with health risk.

The laboratory procedure for determining lean body weight (muscle, bone and organs) versus fat weight is hydrostatic or underwater weighing. It is based on the principle that fat floats whereas lean body tissue sinks, and fat weight is determined by immersing the subject into water to see how well they float. The procedure is time-consuming and involves expensive equipment and so is unsuitable for use in the school setting.

To replace this technique, body fat percentage can be estimated by measuring the thickness of the layer of fat that is stored beneath the skin. Special skinfold calipers (Figure 1) have now been developed which are cheap and sufficiently accurate for use in schools (contact The Physical Education Association for details). The AAPHERD Health-Related Fitness Test (1985) includes a two-site skinfold evaluation of body fatness, and age-related norms tables are available. The testing manual includes detailed instruction on the technique on skinfold reading although it must be cautioned that practice is necessary, especially regarding accurate location of skinfold sites, before confidence should be placed in readings. (For other information on skinfolding technique, see Corbin & Lindsey, 1985).

Many schools now include periodic skinfold measurement so that students can monitor their body fat levels and try to make appropriate changes. Adolescence is a time when great changes in body composition occur. Typically boys will make large increases in muscle bulk, and girls will tend to increase their body fat levels. These changes can be charted quite easily if height, weight and skinfold thickness of each student are measured every six months. In one class period students can record each other's height and weight while the teacher, in a more private area measures, for example, triceps skinfold. Results can be plotted as line graphs on a record card to show the relationships among the three variables. This method has been found to be successful for a number of reasons (Fox, 1983). First, students have a natural curiosity regarding these changes in body dimension and the procedure stimulates interesting discussion. In particular it provides an experience for students through which the concept of body composition can be presented. Second, it allows the identification of any abnormal trends in body composition and provides a basis for individual counselling.

Throughout our chapters in this book, however, we have encouraged means by which students can self-test themselves, with a view to making them 'fitnesss independent'. Accurate skinfolding takes practice, but students can be taught to use skinfold calipers, and very cheap calipers are now available for this purpose. On the other hand, skinfolding is merely a sophisticated version of the 'pinch-an-inch' test as seen in television advertisements. With a sound background in the concepts of body fatness and careful location of skinfold sites on the body, students can get a rough idea of changes in their fatness levels through *manual* (pinching a skinfold between thumb and forefinger) skinfolding. With practice, a ruler can also be used to measure thickness of skinfolds. If this is combined with 'educated' use of bathroom scales, and acknowledgement of any recent changes in exercise patterns, it is possible for students to get a reasonable picture of body composition change without sophisticated equipment. In addition, students can be encouraged to think up other useful tests such as keeping a pair of trim-fitting trousers in storage, and trying them on each birthday. Probably one of the most eye-opening tests of body fatness, for example, is to stand naked in front of a full length mirror and shake about!

What is the role of exercise in body fat control?

Once students have acquired an accurate perception of healthy body fat levels, and through evaluation have established their own levels, they are then in a position to decide what action to take. If they consider that changes are necessary, they need further information before they are fully equipped to design effective and safe methods of altering body composition. This is one of the least understood aspects of health-related fitness and so some time should be devoted to it in the P.E. programme.

Weight loss. Dieting, with a reduction in high calorie food intake, is typically the assumed method of losing fat. Exercise has traditionally been regarded as ineffective because of the slow rate at which it burns calories. It is certainly true that consumption of large quantities of calories by eating is easier than expending them through exercise, but a number of factors make exercise the *key component* of any weight loss programme.

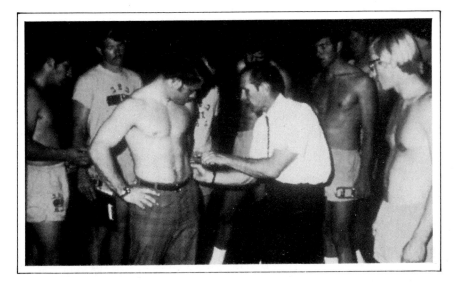

1. Fat accumulates because of long term positive imbalance in calorie intake and expenditure which in 99% of cases is a problem of lifestyle. Short term crash dieting may result in a temporary reduction in weight, but because eating or exercise habits have not been permanently modified, 95% of those who diet soon return to their original weight. Exercise, on the other hand, is a positive move to change one's lifestyle. Changes in activity levels, no matter how small, can make a significant contribution to calorie expenditure in the long run. Walking a mile each day (15 mins.), for instance, will result in the calorie equivalent of 12 lbs fat loss per year. This is much greater that the average gain in fat per year. Many researchers (Bar-Or, 1983) believe that low activity levels is the major cause of childhood obesity, so that students with an overfat problem should be encouraged to be more physically active in all aspects of their daily lives. We know that exercise of adequate intensity (60%+ of maximum) and duration (20-30 minutes minimum) will have the added effect of increasing calorie expenditure for a number of hours *after* exercise has ceased. This is important because we can be receiving the calorie-burning benefits of exercise even when we are relaxing later in the day.

2. It is important to maintain an adequate muscle mass because muscle tissue is responsible for burning calories. Calorie-restricted diets, particularly those low in carbohydrates, deplete energy stores in muscles and tend to produce lethargy with the effect that overall calorie expenditure is reduced—the opposite of what is needed. During these kinds of diets, the body becomes convinced that there is a famine and directs itself to actually preserving body fats as long as it can, for use as a last resort. The body looks for other sources of energy, and muscle tissue that is not being used in regular exercise begins to breakdown and is ingested for energy. The body literally begins to consume itself. There is evidence to suggest that low carbohydrate diets may actually inhibit fat utilisation and speed up muscle wasting. Studies have shown that this muscle wasting does not occur if the diet is accompanied by exercise or if exercise is used by itself as the fat loss agent. The result is that muscle mass is preserved or increased and more body fat is lost.

Many people exhibit a pattern of cyclical crash dieting and regaining of body fat. This regime eventually results in lower muscle mass through gradual wasting, and because fat rather than muscle is regained each time the diet is given up, there is a slow rise in body fat levels. IN EFFECT, FOR THESE PEOPLE, DIETING WILL OVER THE YEARS MAKE THEM FATTER. If they had used exercise in their weight loss programmes, they would be leaner and firmer.

3. Another 'extra' provided by exercise is that it can actually decrease appetite. This is true on a daily basis, where hunger will generally be postponed for a time after exercise is completed.

Bar-Or (1983) also describes how moderate exercise can stimulate a more appropriate appetite response. Below a certain activity level, the body may not respond appropriately and causes the individual to eat more than the activity level requires. With regular exercise, the appetite learns to respond more accurately to the body's needs. In addition, even high levels of exercise do not cause the appetite to rise as much as warranted by the increased calorie usage.

It is clear that exercise increases calorie expenditure *during and after* exercise. Exercise also plays an important role in maintaining muscle mass and creating an appropriate appetite response. It is therefore vital to a fat reduction programme. The most effective type of exercise programme for the reduction of body fat will work at two levels. First, there will be encouragement for general increased daily activity such as walking to school, climbing stairs, bicycling to friends houses instead of catching the bus, and so on, to promote a weekly overall increase in calorie expenditure. Second, time will be allotted to some form of higher intensity activity which will ideally take place three or four times each week to begin with, but which might eventually increase to every day, depending on the activity chosen. The type of exercise most suitable is similar to the activities already suggested for improvement of cardiovascular fitness (see chapter 4). Large muscle group exercise such as walking, cycling, jogging, and lap swimming are most effective at burning calories. If these are performed at an optimal training intensity, they will also maintain or perhaps increase muscle mass and raise resting calorie usage (basal metabolic rate; BMR) for a few hours after each exercise session is completed. Weight-bearing exercise, such as jogging or aerobic dance, is not recommended every day, particularly for the overweight individual, but it is probably safe to swim, cycle, or walk each day if intensity is only

moderate (60-70% of maximum).

Undoubtedly, sensible eating habits also play an important part in maintenance of healthy body composition, and each child should be aware of good nutrition (NACNE, 1983; see also chapter 8), and the dangers of the wide range of diets and equipment which are constantly promoted through the media (ACSM, 1983; Price & Allensworth, 1980). Although it is not possible to comment on all of them here, the gimmickry of the fat loss world should be exposed wherever possible.

Weight gain. There are occasions when it is desirable or even necessary to gain weight. Long term changes can be made through increasing muscle mass or fat stores. Muscle tissue can only be gained by exercising, and the most effective type of activity is strength training. It may be necessary to gain weight for certain sports (usually contact sports) and a fairly intensive weight training programme will be required. Occasionally, an increase in fat stores is desired, and this may be achieved through increasing calorie intake. Increases in quantities of complex carbohydrates, such as pasta, bread and potatoes, is one sensible recommendation, but attention should always be paid to nutritional guidelines. It must be remembered that some ectomorphs may find it difficult to make substantial gains in body weight, and although this might seem a problem in adolescence, it is often a blessing in adulthood. However, potential for largest gains will occur at adolescence. *In cases of suspected anorexia or related disorders, where low levels of body fat have been identified, individuals should be referred for immediate medical supervision.* This is an illness rather than a health-related fitness problem.

How can the physical education programme best promote healthy body composition?

The facts and skills regarding maintenance of a healthy body composition have now been presented, and it is the indisputable responsibility of the physical educator to expose students to this information and provide opportunities to learn fitness skills within the programme. Dealing sensitively with this topic is not easy, however, and takes considerable forethought of the real problems involved if it is to be successful. The whole matter is complicated by an apparent dichotomy. On the one hand we may have a large percentage of students who, for various reasons, are at risk regarding overfatness, particularly later in life. We clearly have to encourage concern for a healthy body for these individuals. Conversely, we appear to have a second sub-group who are susceptible to obsession in its various forms with body shape and composition, to the extent that for the sake of their appearance, they risk ill-health through bad eating habits. In this case we have to educate for more realistic perception and a better understanding of the body fatness problem. Faced with this dilemma, perhaps the following points may help.

1. It is all too evident that we are victims of a "Cult of Slenderness" (Tinning, 1985). It is easy to see that modern society has determined that the 'lean' look is fashionable, with the result that it is socially rewarding to be slim. The media swamp us with a host of messages to suggest that slimness means success, and to

watch some television would leave the impression that 'normal' is to possess a perfect body. Most of us fall victim to fashion and trends, but adolescents, as they search for identities, seem to be particularly vulnerable. This may be especially true for females who tend to lack confidence in their physical selves, and many will be under considerable pressure to display the 'right' image. Although the answers are not simple, as physical educators we need to use our powers to provide a balance to the display of the media, and constantly emphasise that a whole range of body fatness can be considered healthy. We should try to help students develop a realistic perspective by exposing the transience of the fashion world. Comparisons with standards of beauty in different cultures and historical time periods is one approach. For example, Renaissance paintings of the more ample ideal female form of the time can be compared with today's 'perfect' shape. The most important point is that we should try to counteract rather than perpetuate the overemphasis on slimness that surrounds us. We have to carefully tread a fine line between encouraging CONCERN for a healthy body composition, without promoting OBSESSION.

2. Relating to the above discussion, we should reconsider our own perspective regarding body image. Physical educators are characterised by mesomorphy and excellence in physical performance. In this respect the physical education profession has an inbuilt bias in perception of 'normal' body composition and average ability in physical skills. Overfat schoolchildren have traditionally been victims in P.E. programmes, and some studies have shown that children get fatter BECAUSE of involvement in physical education, as it merely serves to reinforce their inadequacy. Other studies have shown that physical educators spend less time with fatter children. To take Tinning's suggestion (1985), perhaps we need

to work within our programmes to help our students feel better about their bodies, and more fully accept a wide range of body types. Weak and overweight children soon become alienated from the type of activities we typically provide, because of their lack of success and frequent exposure to ridicule. Our main objective for such children is to encourage them to actually like physical activity, and we should reshape our attitudes to accepting this kind of child as one of our prime concerns.

3. The problem of body composition is highly personalised, and when dealing with this topic we have to adopt a high degree of professional integrity. Students, especially at secondary level, should be given the privilege of privacy when skinfolding takes place, and they have a right to confidentiality. We must do all we can to avoid embarrasing students and we have to be at our most sensitive if we are to be successful in helping them face problems.

4. There seems little point exposing students to the problems of body composition if we cannot provide an adequate back-up service to help them over their difficulties. The best that we will achieve is to raise some of our students stress levels even higher. Only a minority of students will have body composition problems during their school years. For those fortunate not to, possession of the relevant facts and skills for future use may be adequate, but they should be encouraged to project into the future regarding their levels of exercise, sports, and eating and drinking habits, in order to foresee changes. Those who do have problems, however, should be given the opportunity within the physical education curriculum to operate an exercise programme appropriate for their needs. Certainly, children who have a weight problem can be regarded as requiring remedial physical education, and may benefit from a programme specially designed for them. At present it is unlikely that schools can operate remedial programmes, so it will be necessary to make allowances within existing timetables. Overfat children tend to dislike competitive sports, but integrate fairly well in classes which provide opportunities for individualised activities such as walking, jogging and swimming for fitness. We have been surprised that the type of child who has typically avoided our programmes like the plague soon becomes our strongest ally when he/she realises that support is offered and benefits are there to be realised.

References

AAHPERD, (1985). *Health-related physical fitness test manual*. Reston, Virginia: American Alliance for Health, Physical Education, Recreation and Dance.

AMERICAN COLLEGE OF SPORTS MEDICINE (1983). Proper and improper weight less programmes: A position statement. *Medicine and Science in Sports and Exercise*, Vol 15 (1).

BAR-OR, O. (1983). *Paediatric sports medicine for the pracitioner*, New York: Springer-Verlag.

CANNON, G. & EINZIG, H. (1983). *Dieting makes you fat*. London: Century Publishing.

CORBIN, C. B. & LINDSEY, R. (1985). *Concepts of physical fitness*, (5th edition), Dubuque, Iowa: Wm. Brown.

FOX, K. R. (1983). Teaching physical lifeskills: Practical ideas on health-related fitness. *British Journal of Physical Education*, Vol. 14 (5).

McARDLE, W. D., KATCH, F. I. & KATCH, V. L. (1982). *Exercise physiology: Energy, nutrition, and human performance*, Philadelphia. PA: Lea and Febiger.

NATIONAL ADVISORY COMMITTEE ON NUTRITION EDUCATION (1983). *Proposals for nutritional guidelines for health education in Britain*. London: Health Education Council.

PRICE, J. H. & ALLENSWORTH, D. D. (1980). Guaranteed in just six weeks: Weight loss fads and fantasies. *Health Education, November*.

TINNING, R. (1985). Physical education and the cult of slenderness. *Australian Journal of Physical Education, March*.

This chapter first appeared in the *British Journal of Physical Education*, 1986, Vol. 17(1).

Chapter Eight

Nutrition, Exercise and Health: Food for action, food for thought

Tom Mercer & Stuart Biddle

Educators concerned about the physical fitness, health and well-being of their students will readily recognise the importance of having control over ones' nutrition. As the previous chapter has already outlined, the influences on the diet section of the health-related fitness market-place range from dangerous quackery to sound educational and medical practice. Those involved in promoting health-related fitness have a duty to help students understand the processes of nutrition, in terms of the physiological functions and behavioural control of diet. A well-rounded programme of health-related fitness will teach the A-B-C of well-being: A – activity, B – behaviour, C – consumption (Gillie & Raby, 1984).

This chapter has two main objectives:
(a) to present information on the physiological mechanisms of nutrition, including the proposed links between nutrition and health, and the role of nutrition in exercise, and
(b) to provide some practical guidelines suitable for the self- control of nutrition-related behaviours. Whilst it is accepted that the physical educator has an important role to play in teaching appropriate health-related behaviours, other specialists could also contribute to nutrition education. Obvious examples in schools are staff associated with home economics, science, health education, and the school meal service. A collaborative effort is recommended.

Physiology of Nutrition

The 'convenience ethic' which seems to pervade our society is nowhere more visible than in the area of nutritional supplementation. Typified by a smokescreen of misinformation, the exponents of quackery and food faddism urge us to 'eat all we want whilst still losing weight' or to 'eat brand X with added protein for power packed muscles'! In contrast to that misinformation there is available a steadily growing body of sound nutritional advice. Based on scientific

rigour and from a generally uncompromised standpoint (commercially) this advice should be heeded.

As physical and health educators it is our duty to expose our students to this school of thought which views nutrition as the science of food as it relates to optimal performance and health (Briggs & Calloway, 1984).

Why Eat?

The desire for food originates in the hypothalamus region of the brain. Responding to fluctuations in the levels of certain chemical substances in the body and/or temperature variations, this control centre either stimulates or depresses the appetite. However, independent of physiological mechanisms, psychosocial factors, such as certain social functions, structured mealtimes, and anxiety-stimulated eating binges, also influence food intake (Brooks & Fahey, 1984).

Food itself is defined to be solid or liquid which, when swallowed, supplies nutrients which can perform any or all of the following functions:

(i) to provide body fuel, thus providing the body with sources of energy needed for all its activities

and/or

(ii) to provide materials for the building or maintenance of body tissues

and/or

(iii) to supply substances that act to regulate the body processes (Ministry of Agriculture, Fisheries and Food, 1985).

An awareness of the roles of the different nutrients, combined with a knowledge of the effects of their presence/absence in the diet should be the keystone of sound nutrition education. It is generally accepted that the consumption of about 44-47 nutrients on a regular basis is essential for general good health and well-being. In the interest of realistic nutritional guidance for our students it is much more convenient to group these essential nutrients as follows: carbohydrates, fats, proteins, minerals, vitamins and water. These six classes of nutrients can be conveniently placed into the 3 broader groupings of energy givers, body builders, and regulators (see

Figure 1. Classification of the major nutrients according to their main functions.

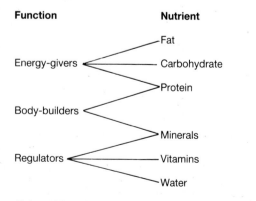

(Adapted from Ministry of Agriculture, Fisheries & Food (1985).

Figure 1). The organization of all the food substances regularly consumed, in terms of quantities of the respective nutrients and the actual pattern of consumption, is what constitutes our diet. This may be considered as the 'gross' mechanism of nutrition.

The consumption of the food initiates the complex processes of digestion and absorption. Digestion ensures that the major nutrients (carbohydrates, fat and protein) are physically and chemically broken down into simpler components (monosaccharides, free fatty acids, and amino acids). The process of absorption then effects the passage of these end-products of digestion through the walls of the digestive tract and into the bloodstream. From here they are transported throughout the body to subsequently contribute to the 'fine' mechanisms of nutrition.

The energy givers

All living things need energy. For humans this need is secondary only to the need for air and water. The nutrients which can serve the body machinery in the role of fuels are fats, carbohydrates, protein and alcohol (produced by the fermentation of carbohydrates). These nutrients can be used more or less interchangeably by the body, depending upon which is more abundant in the diet (Briggs & Calloway, 1984). However, if energy is available in the form of carbohydrate and/or fat in adequate amounts, protein is *not required* to contribute significantly to energy production (Durnin, 1981). Alcohol, on the other hand, is *not able* to contribute to energy production during exercise. In relative terms, fat is able to provide more than twice as much energy as either carbohydrate or protein.

Energy is measured in calories, an often used and misused term. The relationship existing between calories and energy is much the same as that existing between miles and distance, the former merely being a measure of the latter.

Fate and function of carbohydrates in the diet
The carbohydrates found in food can basically be split into two types, simple and complex. The simple carbohydrates include both single (monosaccharides) and double sugars (disaccharides) such as glucose and sucrose respectively. Glucose is present in fruit and plant juices and can also be found in the blood of humans. Sucrose occurs naturally in most foods containing carbohydrate, especially cane sugar. These simple carbohydrates constitute a significant proportion of the total energy contribution of carbohydrates in the diet.

The complex group of carbohydrates are essentially composed of combinations of three or more monosaccharides, thus making them polysaccharides. These may exist in either the plant forms, starch and cellulose, or the animal form glycogen. The former may be obtained in the diet from seeds, peas, beans and a variety of cereals. The animal polysaccharide (glycogen) may be obtained, in small quantities, from animal meats.

An important member of the complex group of carbohydrates is cellulose. This indigestible polysaccharide substance (technically a non-nutrient) is now referred to as dietary fibre. This structural, fibrous remnant of plant carbohydrates, such as fruits and vegetables, performs a necessary regulatory function in digestion. However, the exact mechanisms by which this substance functions remain unclear.

It is important to note that the human body can only use carbohydrates for energy when they are in the form of simple sugars. Consequently starches and complex sugars (disaccharides) must be broken down into simple sugars. These simple sugars are transported by the blood, directly to the liver where they may be:
(i) passed as glucose to all the cells of the body, to be used directly for energy release or
(ii) converted into glycogen (an animal polysaccharide) and stored in the liver and skeletal muscles for future use as an energy supply or
(iii) converted into fatty acids and stored in the body fat as a further source of energy.

Aside from acting as one of the body's major sources of energy, this nutrient functions as a 'metabolic primer', by helping the body to utilize fats efficiently. Carbohydrates also function in a 'protein sparing' capacity by providing energy in order that proteins may be used for more important functions.

Table 1. Features of carbohydrates in the diet.

		Simple	Complex
Structure	:	monosaccharides, disaccharides	polysaccharides
Form	:	glucose, fructose, sucrose	starch, (glycogen) cellulose
Features	:	generally processed (refined).	unprocessed (natural)
	:	similar energy content	
	:	may be found in combination with fats in diet.	generally found in combination with vitamins, minterals and protein.
	:	no dietary fibre.	
Sources	:	confectionary, sugar.	wholemeal bread, vegetables.

Fate and function of fat in the diet
Fats may be classified into three groups simple fats (triglycerides), compound fats composed of simple fats in combination with other chemicals (phospholipids, lipoproteins), and derived fats like cholesterol, which is made from simple fats (McArdle, Katch & Katch, 1981).

The digestion of fat results in the breakdown of triglycerides into free fatty acids and glycerol. The free fatty acids, which are the usable fuel form of the triglycerides, are further transformed by the liver, eventually to be stored in the fat cells (adipose tissue) located throughout the

Table 2. Features of fats in the diet.

		Saturated	Unsaturated
Origin	:	Animal	Vegetable, Fish
Form	:	solid at room temperature	liquid at room temperature
Features	:	similar energy content	
		may stimulate cholesterol production	may inhibit cholesterol production
Sources	:	red meat, butter, cheese, cream.	vegetable oils, white fish, chicken.

The body builders
Proteins and minerals are the nutrients which make the greatest contributions to the continual processes of tissue growth and repair.

Fate and function of protein in the diet
Although it has been stated that protein is relatively low down on the list of preferred body fuels, it can and does make important contributions to energy production. This is especially so in cases of undernutrition (starvation) and may in severe cases cause a 'wasting away' of muscle mass (Durnin, 1981).

The nutrient protein is formed by combinations of simpler substances called amino acids. Twenty-one of these components of protein have been identified. Following digestion of protein these amino acids are able to recombine in a variety of arrangements to form the many different types of protein which the body requires. Interestingly for what seems to be an extremely 'resourceful' nutrient, eight of these amino acids must be obtained from the diet since these so-called essential amino acids cannot be manufactured by the body itself.

Upon entering the bloodstream, after digestion, the amino acids are transported to the liver where:
(i) they may be passed into general circulation as part of the body's pool of essential and

body and within the skeletal muscles (Fox & Mathews, 1981).

The fatty acids may be subdivided into saturated and unsaturated groups. The former are more stable in nature and may be found in most fats. However, the relative proportion in which these 2 types of fatty acids co-exist in any one fat will determine the characteristic of that particular fat. Animal fats tend to contain more saturated fat whilst vegetable and fish oils and fats contain a greater proportion of poly-unsaturated fats.

Whilst fat has been clearly identified as the most concentrated source of body fuel, it is interesting to note that its sole essential function is as the provider of essential fatty acids (Briggs & Calloway, 1984). The role of fat in the diet may be summarised as:
(i) a provider of essential fatty acids
(ii) the body's most concentrated energy source
(iii) a transport medium for fat-soluble vitamins
(iv) as a protective shield, cushioning the vital organs
(v) as an organic insulator, helping to conserve body heat.

non-essential amino acids

(ii) some may be converted into other forms

(iii) some may be used as energy sources.

The ultimate functions of this vital nutrient are:

(i) to act as the 'building locks' of life constructing new cells and tissues, especially during growth, pregnancy, training and in recovery from injury

(ii) in the maintenance of existing tissues

(iii) in the manufacture of substances which control the functioning and regulation of body processes (including enzymes and hormones)

(iv) in the formation of milk

(v) energy production.

Fate and function of minerals in the diet

Minerals are the naturally occurring group of inorganic elements which can be found in soil, water, plants, and in animals. These elements can also be found in our bodies in significant amounts. However, they cannot be formed by the body. Compared to the major organic nutrients (fats, carbohydrates and protein) only tiny amounts of these nutrients are required. However, their presence is essential for the optimal growth and functioning of many body tissues and systems. Minerals can be sub-divided into macro and micro-minerals. The former are required by the body in larger amounts than the latter. The micro-minerals are also known as 'trace- elements' due to their relative presence in the body. Seven macro-minerals have been identified including sodium, potassium, chlorine, calcium and phosphurus. Iron, iodine and zinc are three of the micro-minerals which the body must obtain from the diet.

Generally these minerals enter the diet in the form of mineral salts, in foods, such as sodium chloride (table salt). The range and diversity of function of the 17 or so minerals, essential to a balanced diet, preclude their detailed examination here. (For a more comprehensive examination of the individual functions of specific minerals see Briggs & Calloway, 1984).

Generally, they make important contributions to the growth and development of bone and connective tissue and are important constituents of blood proteins such as haemoglobin and hormones. They also act as soluble salts which help to control the balance of body fluids inside and outside the cells.

The regulators

Whilst minerals also play an important role in this grouping of nutrients the roles of vitamins and water are fundamental to the processes of regulation in the body.

Function of vitamins in the diet

Like minerals these nutrients are required in only minute quantities. As with minerals the functions they perform are integral to good health and well-being. These nutrients may be split into fat-soluble and water-soluble groups. The former, as the name implies, are found in a dissolved form in fats. It is important to note that neither sub-group can be manufactured in the body.

Vitamins were previously classified by letter upon discovery, thus we have all heard of vitamins A, D, E, and K (fat-soluble) along with Vitamins B and C (water-soluble). More commonly, however, they are now referred to by both their symbol (A, B, C etc) and their given chemical name (Riboflavin, Thiamin). Check your cornflakes packet! As with the minerals, the variety of the functions performed by each of the 13 required vitamins in our diet does not permit in-depth treatment here (again, see Briggs & Calloway, 1984, for greater detail). However, as a group their general functions may be categorized as:

(i) promoting growth

(ii) promoting healthy reproduction

(iii) maintaining health, vigour and longevity by promoting:

(a) the use of minerals' amino acids, fatty acids and the metabolism of energy sources
(b) the normal functioning of appetite and digestion
(c) mental alertness and
(d) the health of tissues and resistance to bacterial infections (Briggs & Calloway, 1984).

The importance of water in the diet
The consumption of water by the body is a biological need. Being the major constituent of body fluids it makes up about one-half of the body's weight. Water in the body can be obtained from three sources. It can be consumed as a constituent of solid foods, or as the 'base' of any fluids consumed (tea, orange juice, soup), or it may be produced as a by-product of the body's 'workings' (metabolism).

Primarily, water functions as a transport mechanism in the body by carrying nutrients, waste products, and hormones to and from a variety of tissues. Water also plays a crucial role in regulating the distribution of the mineral salts throughout the body. However, water's greatest contribution is as the body's 'coolant system' in hot environments or during exercise. It is particularly adept at absorbing the heat given off during energy release and subsequently carrying it to the skin to be transferred to the environment.

Nutrition, Health and Weight Control
As with all aspects of health-related fitness the prime concern in nutrition education must lie with prevention – prevention of malnutrition! However, the malnutrition facing Western society is not that which immediately conjures up images of famine or drought-stricken countries, and starving, undernourished children. Ours is the malnutrition of convenience (laziness) and ignorance; the malnutrition of excess (and occasional deficiency). Bad eating in respect of nutrient quantities, qualities, and in the pattern of consumption will inevitably lead to bad health.

What is healthy eating?
It is important to dispel the myth of "health foods". No particular foodstuff has been proven to be a panacea for health. It has long been recognized that 'healthy eating' is more attributable to the increased knowledge available about food, and attitudes towards its consumption, rather than some misguided attempt to concentrate on the specific consumption of a particular foodstuff/nutrient.

A balanced diet involving regular consumption of the six classes of essential nutrients should meet the body's requirements. But what is a balanced diet? Essentially this is a concept based on 'scientific' estimations of the recommended daily intake (R.D.I.) of the key nutrients necessary for good health and well-being. In simple terms we are talking about adequate consumption of energy-givers, body builders and regulators. Eating a wide variety of foods will normally achieve the aims of the 'mythical' balanced diet. However, recent nutritional and medical research has highlighted certain aspects of the traditional Western diet which it is felt could be improved.

Minus three, plus one
The National Advisory Committee on Nutrition Education (NACNE, 1983), having examined

the links between diet and health, has recommemded that generally we should:

    (i) eat *less* fat (especially saturated fats) – to reduce the risk of heart disease

    (ii) eat *less* sugar – to help reduce the likelihood of becoming overweight (overfat)

    (iii) eat *less* salt – to reduce the risk of high blood pressure and

    (iv) eat *more* fibre – to improve the functioning of the digestive system.

The three areas targeted for reduction are all identifiable as potential contributors to coronary heart disease as either primary risk factors (high levels of fat in blood, high blood pressure) or secondary risk factors (obesity). See chapter 3 for more detail. The fourth target area is related to a move towards shifting the major energy contribution of the diet in the direction of starchy carbohydrate consumption instead of fats. An increase of the indigestible carbohydrate remnants (fibre) in the total diet is considered to significantly reduce the risk of chronic intestinal disease.

Weight control

Healthy eating and weight control are inextricably related. Moderate consumption of the major energy-giving nutrients (fats, carbohydrates) will pose no problems. However, caloric imbalance (more energy in than out in this case) will result in fat deposition. Reiterating the advice of chapter 7, prevention of weight (fat) gain is much easier than achievement of weight (fat) loss. Students should be guided to develop an 'early warning' system through regular monitoring of their diets and/or body fat content. For those students who may already be overfat, counselling should be provided. The emphasis should be directed towards programmes of reduced calorie intake in combination with increased aerobic exercise, to achieve desirable fat loss.

However, it should be stressed that not everyone is cut out to be 'Mr or Ms Slender'.

Perhaps it would be better for some older students to remain a few pounds overweight (fat) and be happy, in contrast to being constantly in pursuit of some 'ideal' (unobtainable?) weight or shape, and thus being miserable. Indeed, it is certainly recommended to remain slightly overfat rather than continually lose and regain weight on periodic 'diets'.

Nutrition and Exercise: Food for action

In the quest to gain 'the winning edge' many sports performers have thrown their lot in with nutritional supplementation. Whether it be 'protein packing' or 'mega-doses' of vitamins these performers seem more than willing to put their faith in some 'wonder substance'. Aside from the obvious financial cost and the moral doubts such actions may stimulate (next step steroids?), the fact remains that there is as yet, no known foodstuff (nutrient) which will transform a mediocre, moderately conditioned performer into a winner. Slick advertisers may urge us to 'eat the breakfasts of champions' – but there is no known breakfast likely to make you into one!. Generally, sound nutritional guidance for exercisers, be they competitive or recreational, remains sound nutritional guidance – eat a well balanced diet!

The primary nutritional consideration of anyone involved in exercise should be energy (Wootton, de Looy & Walker, 1986). Essentially the fuels which provide energy for the muscles (the engine of exercise) are carbohydrate and fat. However, their relative contributions to the demands of muscular activity are dictated by a variety of factors including:

> (i) the type of muscular activity; whether it is continuous or intermittent, brief or prolonged, light or heavy
> (ii) the diet; whether it is high or low in carbohydrate and
> (iii) the state of fitness of the individual (Durnin, 1981).

The supply of these body fuels can come from either the diet or from stores in the body. However, evidence seems to suggest that it is the energy stores of the body which provide the link between exercise and performance (Wootton, de Looy & Walker, 1986). During exercise the body is attempting to ensure that the rate at which energy is provided is kept apace with the rate at which it is being used. Basically this equation is hindered by the body's relatively sparse stores of carbohydrate (glycogen). Consequently the contribution of fat as body fuel is crucial to the maintenance of the desired energy balance during exercise. The ability to use fat as a complementary fuel source prolongs the availability of the carbohydrate stores. The respective contributions of these fuels may be summarized, as in Table 3.

Table 3. Body Fuels: Utilization with varying activity.

Exercise Intensity	Exercise Duration	Fuel Used
Maximal (sprint, 400m)	Short	Carbohydrate
Low to moderate (steady jog)	Moderate (< 2 hrs)	Simultaneous use of carbohydrate and fat in equal amounts.
Severe (Marathon)	Prolonged (< 1 hr)	Increased fat Decreased Carbohydrate

The exercising woman

Whilst maintenance of energy sources should be the prime consideration for both male and female athletes, the exercising woman must consider her nutritional status in respect of the identification of 'problem nutrients'. It has been reported that the diet of normal healthy women in the U.S.A. is deficient with respect to the intake of the nutrients iron, magnesium, zinc and vitamin B6. These have been classed the 'problem nutrients' (Hickson & Schrader, 1982).

Iron deficiency in the diet is particularly important with respect to the exercising woman. The consumption of 12-15 milligrams of iron per day is considered essential for optimal function in normal, healthy women (Durnin, 1981). However, this requirement is not always met by the average diet. Iron is an important constituent of haemoglobin, an essential component in the oxygen-binding mechanism of the blood. As such its absence from the diet may lead to impaired oxygen-transporting capacity. Evidence suggests that elimination of iron from the body may be increased, and absorption of iron decreased, in exercising women (Carlmark & Hoglund, 1980). Consequently for the exercising woman, the effects of this potential mineral deficiency may be exacerbated. Therefore a medically supervised course of iron supplementation may be the only remedy.

Promoting Long-Term Behaviours

It is well-known that a very high percentage of individuals who go on a restricted food regimen ("diet") fail to persist with the programme. Not only is regular 'dieting' known to produce possible health problems, it is clearly a poor strategy if *lifetime* health and fitness is desired. The on-off diet syndrome has been called "the rhythm method of girth control" (Mayer, 1968). If one is to teach others, or oneself, a more permanent strategy for the control of body fatness and nutrition, other methods must be sought.

There is a wealth of research on the social and psychological aspects of nutrition and dieting (e.g. Brownell, 1986; Dwyer et al., 1970; Mahoney, 1975; Mahoney & Mahoney, 1976; Mayer, 1968; Striegel-Moore & Rodin, 1985; Stuart & Davis, 1972). Regrettably, little of this information has filtered through to the general public, who remain badly informed by a media infiltrated by quackery (see Harris, 1983). The following strategies are aimed to provide guidelines for the implementation of personal control techniques suitable for lifetime self-control. Such strategies are wholly compatible with the philosophy of this book, that of promoting health/fitness independence for life.

Knowledge and education
Whilst knowledge *per se* is not sufficient to change behaviour, it is an important step in any nutrition education programme. The basic information provided in this chapter, and in chapter 7, will enable people to make more informed choices. Similarly, doubtful commercial practices will be more easily recognised.

Behaviour analysis
An important step in the modification of behaviour is to analyse current practices. Mahoney & Mahoney (1976) suggest that three important 'environments' require attention for individuals who find difficulty in controlling food intake:
  (a) physical environment
  (b) social environment
  (c) personal environment.

The *physical environment* refers to the physical surroundings, and the effects these might have on eating behaviours. For example, clearly visible food is more likely to be eaten, and certain environmental cues, such as watching T.V., can trigger a desire for food.

The *social environment* can also exert a profound influence on eating behaviours. 'Social occasions' nearly always involve food. The custom of offering food and drink to visitors is well-known in our culture. Without making drastic or unsociable changes, it is possible to modify the quantity and type of food offered in a social gathering. This may be particularly necessary fcr Great Britain where many 'traditional' dishes are known to be very high in saturated animal fat.

The *personal environment* refers to personal thoughts and images about nutrition. It is well-known that such thoughts can have a strong influence on our behaviour. Mahoney & Mahoney (1976) refer to this as "cognitive ecology: cleaning up what you say to yourself", while the Campbell's "Turnaround" system recognises the importance of this with a section on "thinking healthy thoughts" (see Campbell's, 1984). Make use of positive self-statements and, on occasions of apparent 'failure' to keep to a well-balanced lifestyle, tell yourself that the situation is under control and that you have the skills to manage. It is important to tell yourself (and feel) that you are in control. Negative thoughts which 'put you down' will not help.

Identifying problem behaviours
Having assessed each of the three environments mentioned above, one needs to identify which of them appears to be a problem area. It is unlikely that just one factor will be a problem – it is more likely that a combination of environmental factors needs modification. Nevertheless, it is important to select out the major problems and tackle them first. For example, although the social and physical environments may be far from 'perfect', the real problem may be in what you say to yourself. This is where you would concentrate your efforts. Table 4 gives some examples of modified self-statements. A more complete discussion of such methods can be found in Mahoney & Mahoney (1976).

Table 4. Possible modifications of negative self-statements (adapted and modified from Campbell's, 1984; Mahoney & Mahoney, 1976).

Negative Self-statements	Modified Self-statements
1. "I don't seem to be losing very fast".	1. "If I maintain my modified *behaviour* patterns, the weight will eventually be lost".
2. "Susan seems to be losing weight much more than me … I guess I'm just not the 'losing' type".	2. "Comparisons with others is meaningless. My own efforts will soon help *me* if I continue on these lines".
3. "I'm naturally overweight; there is nothing I can do about it".	3. "We can't all be the 'perfect shape', but I can modify my weight and keep control of it".
4. "I ate a chocolate bar to-day – I've blown my diet"	4. "Occasional chocolate bars are no problem – anyway, I'll exercise a bit more!"
5. "I'm going to diet to lose fat for the summer".	5. "If I operate comfortable and gradual changes to my current lifestyle, I can lose and maintain a reasonable bodyweight for life".

Performance versus behaviour
An issue which many physical education teachers often fail to recognise is the important difference between health-related *performance* and health-related *behaviour*. In short, it is far more important to try and modify behaviours than it is to produce some transient level of performance. This is true of both exercise (see Chapter 17) and nutrition. As far as nutrition is concerned, therefore, it is better to concentrate on the appropriate behaviour patterns rather than the actual weight change which is desired. If appropriate goal-setting strategies are used (see Wraith & Biddle, 1986), then focus on behavioural goals. Similarly, in the exercise environment, set goals associated with exercise behaviour (e.g. frequency) rather than performance (e.g. number of sit-ups, time achieved). This is particularly important in the early stages of any health-related fitness programme when performance changes will not be readily visible.

Further thoughts on goal-setting
In addition to the important performance-behaviour distinction, other goal-setting strategies need attention. For example, the 'New Year Resolution Syndrome', alluded to in Chapter 17, is often the result of over-enthusiastic and unrealistic goal-setting. Nutrition modification and *lifestyle* changes will only be successful if goals are:
- comfortable and gradual
- short and long term
- realistic, though relatively challenging
- accepted as being important
- given a level of commitment
- monitored and modified from time-to-time
- specific

Experiential learning
Strategies such as those given in this chapter will be much more likely to be implemented if students are given the chance to experience them, as far as is possible, under the guidance of a teacher. Forms of experiential learning, therefore, are important. If group work is limited, individual help should also be given. Similarly, these strategies can be explained and discussed as part of a wider scheme of work on health-related fitness. Chapters 7 and 12 give examples of related work, including self-evaluation cards on height, weight and body fatness, as well as having pupils keep 'logs' on activity patterns, a variety of anthropometric recordings, and dietary habits. All of these, coupled with a sound educational approach to health-related exercise, will provide a well-rounded, balanced and, above all, meaningful

programme for lifetime health and physical fitness.

REFERENCES

BRIGGS, G.M. & CALLOWAY, D.H. (1984) *Nutrition and Physical Fitness* 11th Ed, New York: Holt, Rinehart & Winston.

BROOKS, G.A. & FAHEY, T.D. (1984) *Exercise Physiology: Human bioenergetics and its applications*, New York: John Wiley.

BROWNELL, K.D. (1986) Social and behavioural aspects of obesity in children. In N.A. Krasnegor et al (Eds). *Child health behaviour: A behavioural pediatrics perspective*. New York: John Wiley.

CAMPBELL'S (1984) *The turnaround lifestyle system*. Camden, N.J. Campbell's Institute for Health and Fitness/AAHPERD.

CARLMARK, L.E. & HOGLUND, S. (1980) Iron status in athletes involved in intense physical activity. *Medicine and Science in Sport and Exercise*, Vol. 12(1).

DURNIN, J.V.G.A. (1981) Muscle in sports medicine – nutrition and muscle performance. *International Journal of Sports Medicine*, Vol.3.

DWYER, J.T. et al (1970). The social psychology of dieting. *Journal of Health and Social Behaviour*, Vol.11.

FOX, E.L., & MATHEWS, D.K. (1981). *Physiological basis of physical education and athletics*. New York: Saunders.

GILLIE, O. & RABY, S. (1984) *The Sunday Times ABC diet and bodyplan*. London: Hutchinson.

HARRIS, M.B. (1983) Educating students about obesity: An ounce of prevention, a pound of cure, and a ton of prejudice. *Health Education*, Vol.14 (4).

HICKSON, J.F. & SCHRADER, J. (1982) Female athletes and their problem nutrients. *National Strength and Conditioning Association Journal*, Vol.4 (4).

MAHONEY, M.J. (1975) The behavioural treatment of obesity. In A.J. Enelow & J.B. Henderson (Eds). *Applying behavioural science to cardiovascular risk*. Seattle, Washington: American Heart Association.

MAHONEY, M.J. & MAHONEY, K. (1976) *Permanent weight control*. New York: W.W. Norton.

MAYER, J. (1968) *Overweight: Causes, cost and control*. Englewood Cliffs, N.J.: Prentice-Hall.

McARDLE, W.D., KATCH, F.I. & KATCH, V.L. (1981). *Exercise physiology: Energy, nutrition and human performance*, Philadelphia: Lea and Febiger.

MINISTRY OF AGRICULTURE, FISHERIES & FOOD (1985) *Manual of Nutrition* 9th Impression, London: H.M.S.O.

NATIONAL ADVISORY COMMITTEE ON NUTRITION EDUCATION (1983). *Proposal for nutritional guidelines for health education in Britain*. London: H.E.C.

STRIEGEL-MOORE, R. & RODIN, J. (1985) Prevention of obesity. In J.C. Rosen & L.J. Solomon (Eds). *Prevention in health psychology*. London: University Press of New England.

STUART, R.B. & DAVIS, B. (1972) *Fat chance in a slim world: Behavioural control of obesity*. Champaign, Il: Research Press.

WOOTTON, S., DELOOY, A., & WALKER, M. (1986) *Nutrition and sports performance*. (NCF Resource Pack). Leeds: N.C.F.

WRAITH, S.C. & BIDDLE, S.J.H. (1986) Goal-setting in sport and exercise. *British Journal of Physical Education*, Vol.17 (6).

Chapter Nine

Stress Management

Stuart Biddle & Stephen Pain

"... relaxation is a musculo-skeletal skill which will not only benefit general motor-skill acquisition, but also provides the person with a lifelong fitness skill. The control and regulation of tension will eventually be considered a critical index of 'fitness'" (Coville, 1979, p.177).

In fifty years time when historians trace the development of physical education in British schools, they will find a significant shift of focus in the 1980's. Those teachers committed to this shift recognise two important factors:

  i) that a focus on health needs to be specifically emphasised in the PE programme rather than allowing health topics to be 'covered' incidentally;

  ii) that a focus on health means emphasising a 'fitness for life' philosophy so that students are encouraged to develop appropriate skills, understanding and interest to pursue a lifetime of sensible activity.

With these two factors in mind, teachers appear to be more receptive to expanding their notion of health-related fitness beyond units of work on cardiovascular fitness, circuit training and weight training. Body composition and flexibility are now being increasingly recognised as important factors in lifetime health and fitness, and they are being included to create a broader, more holistic approach (see chapter 1).

An holistic approach is not achieved merely by adding more items of content to a curriculum, however. We believe it is to do with seeing the pupil as a whole person who can develop in many ways. That means that there may be aspects of physical education, largely ignored in schools, which should be studied. We need to consider the many factors which create or undermine a healthy lifestyle. For example, one of the primary risk factors in coronary heart disease (CHD) is hypertension (persistently high blood pressure; see chapter 3). Another risk factor in CHD has been identified as the 'Type A' behaviour pattern,

associated with ambitious, impatient personalities who are also likely to be hypertensive (see Eagle, 1981). Given the health problems likely to be associated with such characteristics, it may be important to identify 'stress management' as an important part of a health focus in physical education. It may be especially important if we consider that all of us are affected to some extent by stress. It has been estimated that stress, or excessive effort, plays a much more important role in cardiovascular disease than has been widely acknowledged (Nixon, 1982).

The main purpose of this chapter, therefore, is to provide a brief background to stress and stress management with a view to practical suggestions for including these concepts in a school physical education programme.

What is stress?

Trying to agree a suitable definition for stress is difficult task – even a stressful one! McGrath (1970) suggested that stress occurs when there is an imbalance between what people think they are capable of and what is demanded of them. This is similar to Csikzentmihalyi's (1975) work when he found that supreme states of enjoyment and involvement were achieved in activities when task demands and personal skills were balanced. Anxiety was caused by a mismatch where too much demand relative to skills caused worry and too little demand brought on boredom and possible anxiety too (see Figure 1).

Stress can be anything which provokes a physiological response from the body, or, as stated by Miller & Allen (1982), "if the homeostatic balance (physiological equilibrium) of the body is disturbed, the individual experiences stress" (p.134).

Of course, it is useful to remember that we cannot, nor indeed do we want to, rid ourselves of stress completely. Selye (1956) reminds us that stress cannot be avoided, indeed we cannot

Figure 1. Stress can result from a mismatch of demands and skills

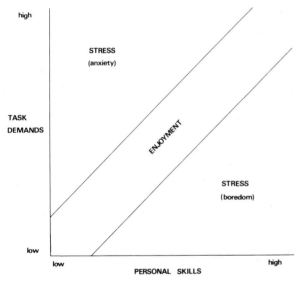

function at all without a certain amount of tension – without it we would lapse into total lethargy. Since we cannot avoid stress, we have to learn to manage it. Indeed, not all stress is harmful or unpleasant. Many people, including physical educationists, actively seek out challenging situations which are potentially stressful in various ways, such as running in races or rock climbing. These people, whose excitement and enjoyment derives from seeking and facing such challenges, and controlling the stress they generate, are known as 'eustress seekers'. However, the perception of what is pleasant or not will, of course, depend on the individual. If you are a potential gold medal winner it may be worth your while to undergo the nerves and then the exhaustion of running a race. If you are an unfit and unathletic fourth year pupil, the annual cross country race may seem less than a good idea! What may seem simple and straight forward, or good fun, to one person may fill another with dread. Perhaps

some physical educationists need to develop their sensitivity and empathy with those who do not share our love of physical challenges.

Unpleasant stress can also be caused by an infinite variety of factors, such as living and work conditions, social relationships, cultural factors, boredom, lack of variety and lack of exercise (see Corbin & Lindsey, 1985).

Reactions to stress

Stress, whether pleasant or unpleasant, will evoke a physiological response. The response may be more obvious in some people than others – for example, the experienced actor will not let stage fright show, while a novice may be a 'bundle of nerves'. Of course, the different ways of responding to a particular situation depend on whether it is perceived as threatening or as pleasantly exciting. Whether one reacts to a situation with fear, or anger, or exhilaration, the response of the body is similar. The body is said to be preparing for 'fight or flight', and specialised chemicals are released into the bloodstream so that the body is made ready for violent action. Expressed simply, the two parts of the adrenal glands, stimulated by the hypothalamus in the brain, and the pituitary gland under the brain, produce hormones called adrenaline, and gluco-corticords, which bring about the well-known 'fight or flight' response, with its increased heart rate, more rapid and deeper breathing, raised body temperature, increased blood flow to the muscles, sweating, increased oxygen utilisation and muscle tension (see Heyward, 1984). Of course, these days it is often not possible to deal with a stressor by fighting or running away, not literally at least. The fight or flight reaction is the first stage of the 'stress response' (Selye, 1956). The second stage is where we resist or adapt to the stressor. If we effectively resist the stressor, ie. by overcoming it or by withdrawing from it, it no longer affects us. If we do not resist or adapt successfully, the stress defeats

us, or it remains as a constant factor. Either way, we may move to the third stage – exhaustion. This stage, where people may strive even harder but achieve less and less, can result in serious illness, including high blood pressure and heart attack. Nixon (1982) has described this pattern as being on the 'downslope' and he has developed effective non-invasive treatments for those who reach this stage. What is more desirable, however, is for all of us to learn to cope with stress at the second stage. It seems to us that learning to control our body's response to something we are bound to meet throughout our lives, is a vital part of a true PHYSICAL education.

Managing stress

Whilst psychologists have long recognised that some individuals have a general tendency towards high anxiety and worry, and, as we have seen, all of us have some tendency to become anxious and stressed, it is also known that a variety of specific stress management skills can play a part in countering the effects of stress. Some of these are based on meditative, or cognitive skills, often including imagery. But there are others involving physical awareness, which may be of more interest to the physical educationist (see Feltz & Landers, 1980). There is insufficient space here to do more than touch the surface of this huge area, but it should be said that there are systems and knowledge of which many of us in physical education know very little. It may be that Tai-Chi, Alexander Technique, Yoga, and other systems have much

to offer in terms of our knowledge of how to care for ourselves. Alexander Technique, for example, may have huge benefits for growing people in terms of learning body management and freedom from tension (see Alexander, 1985; Barlow, 1975).

Two topics are briefly dealt with here: physical relaxation and physical activity.

Physical relaxation

There are many relaxation techniques which have been used in this country and elsewhere. Jacobson's 'progressive relaxation' method has been in use for over 50 years. Used extensively through the Health Education Council's 'Look After Yourself!' (LAY!) classes, this method is simple and straightforward. It is based on the principle that having learned to recognise tension, a person can learn to release or control it. This is a method which can be taught to fairly large groups and then practised by individuals, which makes it very suitable for young people in schools.

The techniques can be learned and practised either lying down or in a comfortable sitting position, but either way it is important that, in the early stages particularly, people are comfortable and warm. It is often useful to conduct classes in a dark or semi-darkened room.

The technique consists of a series of muscle contractions, deliberately held while the person focusses attention on the feeling of tension in the muscle, followed by a conscious release of tension as the muscle is relaxed. For example, the person clenches his or her fists, so creating tension in the forearms. The person concentrates on this feeling of tension for a few seconds, then slowly relaxes the hands and arms, paying attention to the feeling of release and freedom from tension. The procedure is repeated once or twice more with less effort in the initial contraction each time. With practice, people can achieve relaxation quickly without having to carry out the repeated contractions first. The procedure is carried out for all the muscle groups in the body, and it is particularly important that people learn to relax the muscles of the eyes, face and mouth – the muscles used in speech and thought.

The technique, therefore, can be expressed simply in four basic stages:

1. tense muscle
2. recognise tension
3. relax muscle
4. be aware of release of tension.

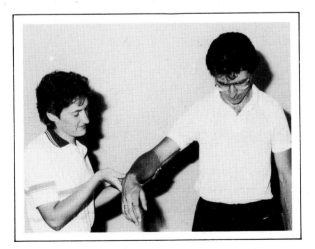

Figure 2.

This method is effective in developing tension awareness and relaxation skills. It does require a series of lessons to be effective, such as that taught through the HEC's 'LAY!' courses. Many teachers have been trained as 'LAY!' tutors and have used these techniques with classes of children with great success. There are also audio tapes available (see Resources section at the end of the chapter) which can assist in the learning and teaching of these skills. A useful class demonstration of the fact that deep relaxation is not easy, and takes time and practice, can be given by using the exercise illustrated in Figure 2. This can easily be done in pairs with a large group of children.

Two people stand side by side, as in Figure 2. The person on the right of the picture induces as much relaxation as possible in their right arm, taking about 30 seconds. The partner then lifts the same arm with one hand under the wrist and the other under the elbow. The person relaxing tries to maintain total relaxation throughout as the partner lifts the arm slowly up to the horizontal (this should take about 10 seconds). Feel the heaviness of the arm at this point. Is it heavy and relaxed or can you feel tension and detect that the individual is 'helping you' with the lifting? Lower the arm slowly, again with the subject attempting to maintain relaxation. Most people will find it very difficult to maintain good relaxation. It is a difficult test of concentration and illustrates that it is particularly difficult to relax in a standing position and shows excessive 'background' tension we may have even when we are not involved in physical work (for other exercises see Corbin & Lindsey, 1985).

Physical activity

As many runners will testify, exercise can also be extremely effective in producing feelings of relaxation, particularly after the run itself. However, competitive activities can sometimes induce feelings of frustration and incompetence

and thus must be treated with some care. The so-called lunch time 'recreation' indulged in by highly competitive squash players, for example, can often produce quite the opposite effect of that intended; ie. a period of 'release' and relaxation. Similarly, many weekend golfers will be aware of the frustrations which can be generated by a missed putt or sliced drive with little at stake except pride!

However, appropriate physical exercise can have beneficial effects for several reasons:

i) there is a strong reduction in muscular tension after vigorous exercise as a compensation for the previous exertions;
ii) vigorous exercise is precisely what the 'fight or flight' stage of the stress response is preparing the body for, so it may be the best way, in certain circumstances, of adapting to a stressor;
iii) feelings of enjoyment, competence and satisfaction can often result from exercise;
iv) exercise can provide a balance of activities alongside work, home responsibilities etc;
v) pleasurable social contact can often result from physical activity;
vi) some activities, particularly prolonged aerobic exercise, have been shown to produce temporary states of extreme, often euphoric, enjoyment, probably due to the production of chemicals called endorphins in the brain (see Sachs & Buffone, 1984; Sacks & Sachs, 1981).

To achieve states of relaxation through physical exercise, one needs to find the appropriate type of activity to suit the individuals' motives for participation. As we have said, what is relaxing for some may be tedious for others, and one person's excitement is another person's terror. Perhaps physical educationists might give more thought to the emotional connotations of activities for different individuals.

Teaching stress management

To introduce a substantial block or unit of work on stress management may seem foreign to the rest of the programme or too ambitious, especially if it is linked to work in other areas of the curriculum, such as tutorial work or health education. However, SIMPLE 'awareness' exercises and relaxation skills can be introduced during other P.E. activities. For example, relaxation procedures could conclude more vigorous bouts of exercise, say after a gymnastics or athletics lesson. In fact, a period of calm should follow after every session of vigorous activity because children should be allowed to experience the 'glow' of feeling good (such as that described earlier). Far too often we rush youngsters through their shower and changing because we are pressed for time. If we want children to feel positive about exercise, we must allow them time to enjoy it.

If a larger work unit is to be introduced, the following guidelines may be helpful:

Objectives:
i) to appreciate that stress management is an important part of a focus on health and a vital 'lifeskill';
ii) to understand the basic causes of stress in life;
iii) to consider the basic links between stress and ill health;
iv) to demonstrate and experience a selection of stress management skills, including relaxation and physical exercise.

Unit 1: Introductory concepts
Concepts: anxiety, stress, 'fight/flight' response,
stress-related illness.
Activities: evaluation of 'how do you feel?'
through questionnaire; individual check list.
Discussion of questionnaire answers in pairs.
Feedback from pairs either to another pair or to
whole group. Teacher records feedback – on
flipchart, OHP, board etc. Which activities are
more/less stressful? Why? Groups of four to
produce short presentation of stress in a
selection of occupations (see Gillie et al., 1982).
Is doing the presentation stressful? What makes
it so?
Relaxation session. Close.

Unit 2: Recognising stress
Concepts: individual differences in the way
people perceive situations.
Activities: evaluation of tension; how do you
feel when you are in a tense situation?
Brainstorm with whole group (list of situations,
list of feelings and 'symptoms' of tension).
Teacher to record. Discussion of different
situations stressful to some but not to others.
What makes it so? Discussion in pairs then from
fours to whole group. Teacher records.
   Draw and describe character stereotypes of
stressed and non-stressed people; invent your
own name: "impatient Iris", "competitive
Clive", "sedate Sid" etc.; describe their lifestyles
and ways in which they do or do not cope with
stress. Say what you think will happen to them
and say how they might change their lives;
what help might they need to change?
Relaxation session. Close.

Unit 3: Coping with stress
Concepts: relaxation; tension.
Activities: identification of 'positive' v 'negative'
"coping strategies". Brainstorms for lists of
strategies; discussion of merits of particular
methods, (eg. exercise v drugs); in pairs with
feedback to another pair. Describe and discuss

feelings (relaxation/tension ...) before and
during different physical activities. Identify the
types of activity and suggest what it may be
that causes particular feelings. Discuss in
groups of 5 or 6; each group member has an
opportunity to disclose true feelings if they
wish. Practical experience of different activities
can be recalled or arranged to illustrate the
points.
   Experience progressive muscular relaxation
and heart rate monitoring, especially in reaction
to preparing to run a race, giving a talk to the
whole group etc. (BBC microcomputer software
is available for the monitoring of physiological
responses. This makes for a good class
demonstration; see software section in
Resources list at the end of the chapter).

Unit 4: Pleasurable stress seeking
Concepts: eustress v. dystress
Activities: identification of activities which are
'exciting' or 'anxiety producing'; brainstorm to
produce list followed by discussion. Discussion
of 'dare devil' activities – 'playing chicken' etc;
what makes people do them? How can you
resist pressure if you really don't want to do a
risky thing without losing face? Opportunity to
role play here, if group and teacher are ready.
Suggested situation – group of children are
encouraging one (younger?) child to swing on a
rope across a deep river. Discuss or role play:
'what would you do?' 'How would you feel?'
Relaxation session; heart rate monitoring. Close.

Assessment of work (if desired):

select from: a) short quiz; b) short essay – either factual (ie. on a topic from the course), an account of a person's reations to the course, describing feelings and what they have learned; creative/descriptive piece illustrating the concepts which have been discussed; c) demonstration and explanation of relaxation skills.

Teacher resources: see end of chapter.

We do not claim that the guidelines just given are a complete course. They are merely illustrative of a suggested approach.

Conclusion

We believe that stress and stress management should be an integral part of the focus on health within the physical education programme. However, some teachers may remain unconvinced of its place within their work. Some of the reasons for this may be:

a) lack of knowledge about stress management;
b) doubts about the importance of stress management;
c) doubts abouts its relevance within P.E.;
d) lack of confidence about teaching stress management;
e) a view that physical education is about vigorous activity, and particularly sport.

We would argue that a true or complete PHYSICAL education must be concerned with all aspects of an individual's development in terms of knowledge and experience of matters affecting it. That includes matters to do with health and fitness as well as sport, and stress management is an important part of keeping healthy.

It could be argued that it does not matter where in the school curriculum such material is taught, as long as it is. However, it has been suggested very eloquently elsewhere (Fox, 1983) that the P.E. teacher has a unique role to play in helping young people to develop 'physical life skills'. The learning of stress management skills through exercise and relaxation techniques, and the understanding that goes with it, is, or at least should be, part of that process.

If we are talking about skills with application to the 'real world', then it may be that lifeskills, such as stress management, have a stronger claim to relevance than some of the more traditional P.E. activities.

HRF teaching, and now a broader focus on health in the P.E. programme, came about partly because of the excessive and still rising levels of degenerative disease which could, to some extent at least, be associated with lack of physical activity. This new focus also came about because of general dissatisfaction with traditional programmes, which clearly were not a complete preparation for a lifetime of sensible exercise. Perhaps we should take the lead in teaching stress management, and in investigating the range of systems and techniques, before the rise of stress-related illness forces us to do so.

References
ALEXANDER, F.M. (1985). *Use of the self.* London: Gollancz.
BARLOW, H. (1975). *Alexander principle.* London: Arrow.
BENSON, H. (1977). *The relaxation response.* London: Fount.
COVILLE, C.A. (1979). Relaxation in physical education curricula. *The Physical Educator*, Vol. 36.
CORBIN, C.B & LINDSEY, R. (1985). *Concepts of physical fitness* (5th Ed). Dubuque, Iowa: Wm.C. Brown.

CSIKZENTMIHALYI, M. (1975). *Beyond boredom and anxiety*. San Fransisco: Jossey-Bass.
EAGLE, R. (1981). *Taking the strain*. London: BBC Publications.
FELTZ, D.L. & LANDERS, D.M. (1980) Stress management techniques for sport and physical education. *Journal of Physical Education and Recreation*, February.
FOX, K.R. (1983). Teaching physical life skills: Practical ideas of health-related fitness. *British Journal of Physical Education*, Vol. 14(5).
GILLIE, O. et al. (1982). *The Sunday Times new book of body maintenance*. London: Mermaid.
HEYWARD, V.H. (1984). *Designs for fitness*. Minneapolis: Burgess.
McGRATH, J.E. (Ed) (1970). *Social and psychological factors in stress*. NY: Holt, Rinehart & Winston.
MILLER, D.K. & ALLEN, T.E. (1982). *Fitness: A lifetime commitment*. Minneapolis: Burgess.
NIXON, P.G.F. (Sept 1982). Stress and the cardiovascular system. *The Practitioner*, Vol. 226.
SACHS, M.L. & BUFFONE, G.W. (Eds) (1984). *Running as therapy: An integrated approach*. Lincoln, Ne: University of Nebraska Press.
SACKS, M.H. & SACHS, M.L. (Eds) (1981). *Psychology of running*. Champaign, Il: Human Kinetics.
SELYE, H. (1956). *The stress of life*. NY: McGraw-Hill.
WALKER, C.E. (1975). *Learn to relax: 13 ways to reduce tension*. Englewood Cliffs, NJ: Prentice Hall.

Teacher Resources

In addition to the references shown above, the following resources may be of assistance:

Books
Bassey, E.J. & Fentem, P.H. (1981). *Exercise: The facts*. Oxford University Press.
Diagram Group (1978). *The complete book of exercises*. London: Arrow Books.
Jacobson, E. (1978). *You must relax*. NY: McGraw-Hill.
Madders, J. (1979). *Stress and relaxation*. London: Dunitz.
Mitchell, L. (1977). *Simple relaxation*. London: Murray.
Polunin, M. (Ed) (1981). *The health and fitness handbook*. London: Sphere.

Tapes
"Relax – and enjoy it!". Dr Robert Sharpe, Lifeskills, 3, Brighton Road, London N2 8JU.
"Just relax". Mathew Manning, Mathew Manning Centre, 39, Abbeygate Street, Bury St Edmunds, Suffolk.
"The fairy ring". Mike Rowland. Meditation and relaxation music. Mathew Manning Centre (see above).
Yendell, P. (1981). *Taking the strain*. BBC record and tape.

Software
Biogram diskette (including relaxogram program). For BBC Micro model B. From Synergy Software, 7, Hillside Road, Harpenden, Herts AL5 4BS, tel: 05827 2977.

Section C

Teaching Health-Related Fitness

Chapter Ten

Getting Started in Health-Related Fitness

Ken Fox, Jim Whitehead & Charles Corbin

The purpose of our chapters in this book has been to provide a sound scientifically-based rationale, not only to convince physical educators of the worth of fitness education, but to help them *defend* it. An important part of this presentation has been to summarise the wealth of research evidence that now substantiates the need to include fitness in the curriculum. Wherever possible, the chapters have attempted to orientate the information towards the real practical problems faced in the school setting. To achieve these aims, we have relied heavily on the American and Canadian growth in health-related fitness research and applications in schools, in order to learn from their successes and also their mistakes. There are examples of fitness programmes which have been successful in making long-term improvements is student's fitness and exercise orientations, which are still evident many years later (Slava, Corbin & Laurie, ,1984). It is equally clear, however, that programmes can not only be ineffective in making lasting changes, but can also be detrimental to the future fitness welfare of students, particularly where a sound educational philosophy has not been adopted. Cautions have been offered against these misapplications.

It is hoped that these chapters have provoked, persuaded, and also provided guidelines for those physical educators interested in introducing health-related fitness concepts into their curriculum. The encouraging response and reaction to the articles, as they appeared in the *British Journal of Physical Education*, as well as a noticeable general emergence of interest within the profession, has convinced us that a large number of schools are ready to take up the challenge and make appropriate changes. Many schools are already involved and committed. The result is that the most frequently raised questions are now concerned with the 'how' rather than the 'why' of health-related fitness. Teachers are actively seeking practical advice.

This chapter will suggest strategies that will help override some of the more common initial difficulties in implementing programmes, and hopefully provide momentum for success. It would be unwise to recommend a standardised operating protocol for all schools to adopt because each situation is different and requires independent evaluation. It is also wasteful for a chapter such as this to become over-involved with specifics. There is too much to say which has general value. A variety of approaches are presented here (some of which are already functioning in schools successfully) so that the practitioner can select the most appropriate direction to take.

Before a curriculum plan can be developed, a careful look at the nature of the content of fitness education must be taken.

Content of the Programme

Throughout our chapters three different facets of content have emerged which can be represented as steps for students to take up the stairway to lifetime fitness (see Chapter 1). It is recommended that consideration be given to all three steps in a health-related fitness programme. All are vital if we are to expect students ultimately to become 'fitness independent'. Referring to Figure 1, these are:–

Step 1: Knowledge foundation

It is clear that students need to be fully informed of the *fitness facts*. Although research has consistently shown that fitness knowledge alone is not a good predictor of exercise behaviour, this does not preclude it from influencing behaviour. There are many examples to support this, as in the case of the overfat boy who begins aerobic exercise because the facts tell him that it will help him lose body fat, or the girl who begins weight training once she finds out that she will not develop huge muscles. More important though is the way that knowledge helps shape our beliefs and attitudes, and allows us a scientific foundation on which to operate fitness skills. We suggest that the facts of exercise be taught, but using teaching methods which ensure relevance to each student, and integration wherever possible with the learning of fitness skills. For example, in order to understand the purpose and action of the basic exercises such as a bent-knee sit-up, it is necessary to be familiar with simple muscle kinesiology such as the function of the abdominal muscles. If we are to persuade students of the prevalence and dangers of coronary heart disease, it is essential to understand the nature of a heart attack. Students are curious and concerned about their physical selves and this material becomes very interesting when it is made relevant to them personally, and also to their parents and friends.

Step 2: Experiencing exercise
It is vitally important that students are given the opportunity to experience exercise in its various forms. The practical section of a health-related fitness programme should expose students to the type of exercise that will promote each part of fitness. Weight training, aerobic dance, circuit conditioning, stretching, introduction to jogging, swimming for fitness, are all examples of practical mini-courses which can be made available.

Enough practice should be given to allow students to develop confidence in their ability to design warm-ups and sequences of calisthenics etc. Sports and games classes can also be orientated to the relevant fitness concepts, and still allow time for the sport-related skills that are usually covered. Of course, a balance of enjoyment AND understanding should be the key element in all exercise experiences.

Step 3: Fitness and lifestyle problem-solving skills
The ultimate goal of the programme is to teach those fitness skills which allow students to regulate their own fitness behaviours. Self-testing and monitoring of all parts of health-related fitness should be a skill that all children have mastered by the time they leave school. Similarly, exercise prescription skills, the ability to deal with injuries, and a basic understanding of the mechanisms involved in motivation and behaviour change, will help equip students for fitness independence. The capacity to critically analyze the fitness consumer market of books, magazines, equipment, and fitness facilities in the area, will help students make intelligent and informed decisions regarding their future exercise. These decision-making and problem-solving skills may also be applied to nutrition and stress management behaviour.

Clearly, the three steps described here are not independent. Knowledge based on sound evidence provides the foundations on which students might better understand their exercise

FITNESS PROBLEM SOLVING

Fitness independence
Self-regulation & motivation
Self-evaluation
Prescribing exercise
Planning programmes
Exercise consumerism

EXERCISE EXPERIENCE

Calisthenics	Sports for fitness
Weight training	Fitness for sports
Stretching	Swimming for fitness
Aerobics	Effective exercise
Jogging	Correct exercise
Circuits	Incorrect exercise

KNOWLEDGE FOUNDATION

Importance of:—	Skill v Health-related	Fitness levels
strength	fitness	Exercise myths
muscular endurance	Coronary heart disease	Correct exercise
cardiovascular fitness	Nutrition & exercise	Wrong exercise
body composition	Stress & relaxation	
care of back & posture	Exercise injury & treatment	

Figure 1: Example programme content

experiences. Both knowledge and experience then go towards developing the more abstract cognitive skills of exercise decision-making and fitness problem-solving. In addition, it may be feasible to deal with all three steps while dealing with any particular part of fitness. If flexibility is the topic, for example, information on stretching can be taught alongside practice with simple flexibility tests and stunts, and followed by the design of a stretching programme. It would, however, be logical to work from a knowledge foundation upwards, with problem-solving skills as an end product. Special consideration also needs to be given to young children below middle school age, as the more abstract aspects of Step 3 may be beyond their stage of cognitive functioning (see chapter 12).

A Choice of approaches

The content featured in Figure 1 can be taught in many different ways. The approach used will depend on:–
1. Level of commitment of yourself and your P.E. department to health-related fitness.
2. Experience with health-related fitness.
3. Degree of support of administration and other members of staff.
4. Curriculum time available.
5. Facilities and teaching resources available.
6. Age and number of students.
7. Whether the course is to be optional or required for all students.

We feel it important to comment at this stage that *the ultimate goal should be to provide a comprehensive fitness education for ALL students.* We suggest that a binding commitment to this principal at the outset is necessary to overcome the difficulties which normally present themselves. Given ideal circumstances with few constraints, the task of change should not be too difficult and a fully committed plan covering all the aspects previously discussed can go ahead. However, we know that such situations are rare, and more typically resources and

The Principal and Chairman of the Governors try a fitness test.

facilities are limited, and support from colleagues not readily forthcoming. On some occasions, a less ambitious approach to begin with might provide the initial success necessary for more extensive involvement in the long term.

A variety of approaches have already been successfully applied in British schools. These offer a choice ranging from a small degree to high degree of immediate curriculum change.

A. Extra-curricular

An excellent example of extra-curricular work has been reported by Keith Bailey (1985). Guest speakers were invited to give presentations to students on topics such as 'looking after yourself', exercise physiology, sports injuries, fitness and performance. The overall objective was to present an insight in to health and fitness for students in order to encourage positive attitudes. Student involvement was an integral part of the activities and a "marvelous response" from students was the outcome.

The advantages of an introductory package

such as this are enormous. Primarily, it acts to stir up interest among students, but probably of more promotional significance is that it makes administrators and other staff aware of the interests of the P.E. department. As will be discussed later in this chapter, convincing colleagues may be vital to the acceptance of a health-related programme in the curriculum. Also, a short course such as this is probably the easiest and most effective way of pilot testing the possibilities for health-related fitness in the programme. Its success may be enough to stimulate discussion about the provision of curriculum time for a course designed for all students, yet it requires relatively little in terms of resources and time. In the case of Wanstead School (Bailey, 1985), a much more comprehensive within-curriculum health-related fitness programme has now been implemented as a result of their initial success.

B. A Re-orientation

Within the existing programme of more traditional games, sports, and gymnasium activities, it is possible to re-orientate each lesson or group of lessons with an approach more consonant with information and principles involved in health-related fitness. Examples might be: teaching the importance of warm-up during a soccer lesson, or expounding the virtues of jogging for cardiovascular fitness and fat loss within a cross-country unit. Of course, we suggest that this be a necessity of any health-related fitness programme, but for some, it may provide a significant move towards accepting health-related fitness as a vital part of the programme. Its advantage lies in the fact that it requires little or no administrative reorganisation and can be tackled by teachers on an individual basis, perhaps where little interest or support is offered from other staff. The disadvantage is that the information is inevitably offered at a superficial level, and often in a piecemeal fashion which is limited in

its impact, and often confusing for students. It does, however, give teachers the opportunity to 'experiment' with ideas, and may be a suitable approach at primary level where concepts should be much simpler and the emphasis on enjoyment of the activities. If organised well, it could provide an opportunity to integrate fitness and exercise concepts with the daily games and movement activities which tend to be the pattern in primary school physical education (see chapter 12).

C. Block or modular approach

Len Almond (1983) has suggested that a possible approach for some departments is to design a module on health-related fitness, and timetable this as a block or unit of work within the existing P.E. programme. An ideal time may be in late Autumn or early spring when the weather is poor. The advantage of this approach is that it provides a convenient package which can be planned well in advance (summer term). Resources can be developed, and classrooms as well as P.E. facilities can be timetabled if they are available. The extra workload and commitment required to launch a unit such as this is not heavy because the amount of new material for teachers is unlikely to be overbearing. Suitable resources are already in existance for the operation of units like these (Corbin & Lindsey, 1983). We feel that the disadvantage in this approach is that health-related fitness concepts deserve a worthier role than being an 'appendage' attached to the main body of the programme. To be totally effective, they must underly the whole of the P.E. programme as an essential theme or justification for the involvement of students in physical activity. Such a module, however, may operate well as a pilot project or first attempt at teaching health-related fitness within the curriculum.

D. Extended course on health-related fitness

For those who wish to face the trauma of a

higher degree of change, and who are able to win colleague and administrative, as well as student and parental support, creating and timetabling an extended course for the specific intention of promoting lifetime fitness of students may provide an answer. Experience has shown that this may provide a tough starting point, and risk of failure may be high.

Rawlins Community College in Leicestershire, under the leadership of Chris Worcester, has attempted to create a health-related fitness course for all 4th and 5th year upper school students. The course got off to a somewhat dubious start in 1979, but was gradually refined and improved as experience and resources accumulated, and teacher confidence grew. The programme is presently enjoying a good deal of success. Additional curriculum time outside normal P.E. time was acquired for this classroom/laboratory course which rotated with careers and R.E., so that 4 units of 10 lessons are taught (2 lessons for 5 consecutive weeks), giving 40 lessons in all over 2 academic years. In addition, practical options, which are specifically designed to promote 'good' exercise and fitness, are offered alongside a variety of sports. For those interested, this programme has been reported elsewhere (Fox, 1983b).

A similarly extensive commitment to exercise and fitness education and its integration with health education has been launched at Frodsham High School in Lancashire. John Hayward and Martin Smiddy have constructed a course across years one to five and report (personal communication) that by the time pupils reach the 5th year, they will have pursued two six-week fitness courses and two two-week introductory courses in the 1st and 2nd years. Fifth year students are then placed on a 'negotiated fitness' scheme where they are working towards fitness independence.

E. Local Authority Involvement

A good example of local authority intervention is provided by Coventry L.E.A., where, through its advisory board, the authority has played a major role in promoting health-related fitness education in the curriculum. Funding has been provided for the development of resources and a project officer appointed to oversee developments. This may be a worthwhile line of approach in some local authorities and it is recommended that department heads consult with their advisers regarding the possibilities.

This list of approaches is obviously not exclusive. Whatever the direction taken, we recommend (on the principle that success breeds success) that it is probably wise to start small and do a good job, than have to backtrack after taking on too much. It is much easier to lose than gain credability. On the other hand, we hope that readers might 'think big' in the long term and be committed to a comprehensive programme for all students, and perhaps additional provision for special populations. Too frequently we have found physical educators who have boasted that for years they have included fitness concepts in their programmes. On analysis, often their curriculum organisation for fitness education is very limited, with the result that fitness skills are at best a by-product of other activities. A comprehensive plan is ultimately necessary in order to fully meet objectives. We do find though, that getting started in health-related fitness is the most difficult hurdle, and the success and rewards that accompany this type of approach tend to increase motivation for further change. So be prepared!

Helping Change Go Well

1. Knowing where your stand

Most people are naturally resistant to change. It makes them feel uneasy because it involves uncertainty, and holds the threat of new challenges. Consequently, unless the benefits can be clearly seen to outweigh the risks, there follows a natural (and very sensible) tendency to question new ideas and resist change. In terms of gaining acceptance to a proposed new health-related fitness programme, the best way of convincing doubting colleagues, parents, or administrators, is to have a sound professional *philosophy* that encapsulates all the answers to questions and criticisms. One such philosophy is based on the premise that health-related fitness offers *unique* and *essential* benefits to our students, which are the sole concern of P.E. (rather than, say, drama or science), and cannot, therefore, be ignored in a complete curriculum (see Chapter 11).

Obviously there are other equally valid philosophies, and change will occur anyway due to new situations and circumstances. The important thing though is to *have* a philosophy which hopefully will be based on an up-to-date knowledge of the relevant facts, and is logically constructed, so you are armed to defend yourself against all critics and doubters!

2. Organising resources, equipment and facilities

There are many good books available which can help build up a store of knowledge of health-related fitness. Many of these have been referenced in this book, and readers are invited to look back over our previous chapters. Many journals, magazines, and even newspapers contain excellent articles which can be collected, and even used for handouts. Television programmes on fitness and health are being screened regularly these days, and might well be worth video-taping for future showing. Local Health Education Offices are usually very helpful with a variety of materials and often can help direct you to other sources of free material which are produced by commercial sponsors such as the Dairy Council or Flora margarine. Collection of these resources tends to snowball as each new source opens new horizons of knowledge, and suggests further references to be explored. As the library expands, its worth will be appreciated. Nobody can pretend to

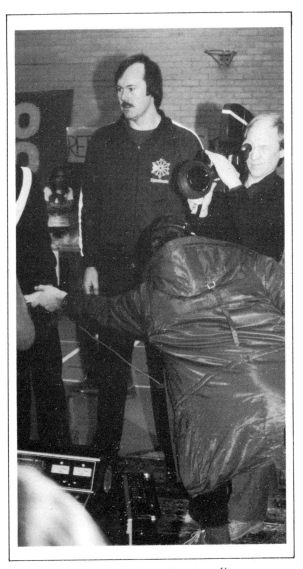

Innovative programmes may attract media coverage.

know all the answers relating to health-related fitness as it spans a vast area of the sciences from psychology to physiology. When a problem or difficult question arises, a file of references is invaluable. Materials can even be lent to colleagues who hopefully, in turn, will become motivated to explore and add their contribution to the library. Most school libraries have an annual budget for book and journal purchases. If the P.E. department isn't claiming its fair share, now might be the best time to start.

Experience has shown that acquiring a room that can be converted into some sort of fitness classroom/laboratory can be extremely valuable. This can provide a central base for resources and equipment and it may be possible to use the facility for the more classroom oriented health-related fitness activities such as demonstrations, simple fitness tests and stunts, and to teach exercise facts. The room can be made unmistakeably fitness-oriented by posters and bookshelves with pamphlets and materials which can be taken away. Probably as important might be the fact that a room such as this can represent the commitment that the physical education department has made to the teaching of health-related fitness, acting as a kind of flagship for other staff to notice.

Health-related fitness can be taught with a minimum amount of new equipment, and can provide an extremely inexpensive addition to the curriculum. Initial cost, therefore, should not be prohibitive in any school situation. Some equipment, however will help give the health-related fitness programme a boost. A good quality skinfold caliper (such as Harpenden) for estimation of body fatness, and a bicycle ergometer (such as the Monarch) will help in demonstrations of fitness concepts, and are also necessary if serious fitness testing is going to be considered. A heart rate monitor, such as Cardiometer, a blood pressure cuff with digital read-out, and sit-and-reach flexibility boxes will also be useful additions. To many students and staff, the appearance of such equipment at this is fascinating, and helps them appreciate the scientific basis of health-related fitness. To aid student participation and provide opportunities for self-evaluation practice, cheap but reasonably accurate plastic skinfold calipers can be purchased, and it is easy to construct basic versions of the sit-and-reach box for general class use. An accurate set of weighing scales and a number of height measures (marked on the door or wall) are also very useful, and physiology charts and models can often be acquired on indefinite loan from the biology department. The cost for a health-related package of equipment such as this should be less than a thousand pounds, and the equipment can be collected as money is available over a number of years. Compared to the percentage of capitation allocated to renewal of sports equipment each year, or the cost of team transportation, health-related fitness provides a very cheap addition to the programme. Catalogues of health-related fitness equipment are now available in Britain from the P.E.A.

3. *Communicating ideas to colleagues*

The key to the success of any health-related fitness venture is primarily the dedication of the whole of the P.E. department to the cause. The initial task of the innovator is to convince other P.E. colleagues of the philosophy and worth of a comprehensive health-related fitness education. Experience has shown that this is not the easiest of tasks and patience is probably a necessary virtue when asking colleagues to make a change in their orientation. To be realistic, the process may take a number of years, and in some cases may never happen at at all. Some colleagues simply lack confidence and this may not be immediately obvious as it often expresses itself in a stubborn resistance to change. In this case, a very subtle helping hand will be necessary to help colleagues experience success, and often these doubters will become your strongest allies. Certainly many colleagues can be convinced by setting a good teaching example for them to model. A successful one-person mini venture into health-related fitness might be helpful in some situations. Constant discussion, and presentation of ideas, articles, and texts, is about the best ammunition available for persuading colleagues to take on a new venture.

Very often, decisions on new courses, and the allocation of curriculum time and resources within a school, depend on the level of support from colleagues outside the PE department, as well as within. The basis of a good public relations job is *communication* of the worth of your proposed new venture to others. This can be achieved both by subtle and overt means. In the former case, a real effort can be made to talk to colleagues from other departments, the head and his/her deputies, and parents and school governors, whenever they are available. There are few people who are not interested in their own personal fitness levels, and schoolteachers are no exception. Even though many are not fit, most show a concern for their fitness. There are not many real experts to consult, as doctors seem to know more about illness than fitness, and physical educators have typically shown more expertise in the coaching of sports skills. Being available for fitness advice to other staff will give opportunities for discussion, and offering a fitness testing and exercise advice service will be a professionally rewarding exercise as well. At Rawlins College, the Principal and Chairman of the Governors came to be fitness tested together, and as well as being enlightened about their own fitness levels, they became firm advocates of the department's programme. If there is sufficient interest, it might be helpful to provide lunchtime or after-school fitness activities for staff such as jogging, weight training, indoor soccer, or swimming for fitness sessions. If staff enthusiasm for fitness and activity can be nurtured and supported in this way, they will become strong advocates of the worth of a student health-related fitness programme.

A second means of communication of your philosophy and curriculum plans, is to give formal slide presentations to groups such as staff, parents, governors, or even local P.E. conferences. Everybody has probably experienced sitting through presentations that either have no visual aids, or just poorly prepared overheads, and the worth of good slides thus needs no further explanation. (Once collected, they are also of great value for day-to-day teaching as well). Gaining the interest of the local PE adviser is also highly recommended. Advisers exist to counsel, assist, and support teachers. They also have many valuable resources and powers to enable them to do so. A friendly adviser may help you with your presentations, and might even wish to actively promote your innovation if convinced that it is worthwhile. Finally, local P.E. departments of colleges, polytechnics and universities can give support also. You may already be helping them by providing teaching practice for their students, so why not ask for some favours in return?

4. Helping Colleagues feel successful
    The threat of having to teach new material has already been touched upon. If classroom lessons are to become a feature of the new programme, the additional unease may stem from having to operate in what is, for some P.E. teachers, an unfamiliar environment. (Imagine how classroom teachers might feel in the gym, or on the sportsfield). In the early stages of teaching health-related fitness, most teachers require a high degree of structure and a great deal of prepared material, because, understandably, they do not feel familiar with the area: good forward planning and regular presentation of example lesson plans by the department 'expert' should be very helpful. If there is nobody confident or experienced enough to do this, then outside help in the form of in-service training will be necessary. If this is not available, then request it through your P.E. adviser or write to the P.E.A. In the near future, through bodies such as the P.E.A. and Loughborough Health-Based P.E. Project, it is hoped that many more in-service courses will be offered. Increased demand will ensure this.
    Many colleagues will enthuse once they feel that they are part of the programme and their efforts, resources, and abilities have been responsible for the programme's success. A

democratic outlook and organisation is the key here. Regular weekly meetings where problems are aired and communication channels opened up will help expose areas that need attention. A new course inevitably means a heavy work load of preparation of new materials. This load can be eased considerably if it is shared, and, ideally, each teacher can research and prepare a particular area of interest, and then present their 'unit' to the others in the department during regular team meetings. Familiarisation with new topics and approaches can be facilitated by team teaching if the timetable allows. One excellent way to learn new approaches to some aspects of a new course is to have outside speakers teach classes whenever possible. Many experts and 'personalities' in the local community are surprisingly willing to give time and effort in their areas of interest. Observation of their style and approach, as well as gaining from their knowledge, can add to any teacher's skills. Qualified experts can also be requested to give in-service sessions to the whole department. Liaison with the P.E. adviser can help here, but, very often, a direct approach to local Health Education Offices, college, polytechnic and university departments, and even hospitals, can be fruitful. (Sometimes they will loan or even donate expensive equipment, especially if it is somewhat obsolete in their better funded institution). Staff from other departments in the school might also wish to be included in any in-service 'teach-ins' that are arranged, if they are relevant. For example, the Home Economics team might wish to attend a nutrition session, and many staff might gain from a first-aid or sports injury presentation.

5. Publicity: spreading the word

Don't be afraid to let people know what you are doing. The objective of a Fitness for Life programme is educationally sound and can only gain credit. One indirect method of publicity results from students discussing their lessons with parents. Many good materials, such as pamphlets and booklets, can be purposely designed or obtained free from outside agencies (e.g. the Health Education Council). A common result of this information reaching parents, is a demand for more information from them. At Rawlins School and Community College in Leicestershire, this demand resulted in the start of adult evening classes, and a community fitness testing and prescription service. Do make sure that materials are well prepared and contain information that is scientifically sound.

Around the school, try to make good use of noticeboards and display areas. Much good educational information can be disseminated in this way, as well as focusing worthy attention on your efforts. Regular announcements in staff meetings, both formal and informal, about current fitness events and achievements also raises awareness amongst colleagues. P.E. teachers traditionally announce sport success in the staff room, and an edifying perspective to your efforts can also be communicated if mention of 'problem pupils' efforts are related as well. If a previously recalcitrant pupil has made an effort in your new programme, then tell other staff, and request them to give praise for this effort. Similarly, if an overfat or weak child has succeeded in overcoming his/her physical problem, then this tremendous achievement should be given the credit it deserves. The effect can be beneficial all round as the physical education department will be seen as catering for all students rather than being limited to sporting excellence.

Once a programme is running well it is also a good idea to allow students to critically evaluate it. It is our experience that health-related fitness has such a high personal interest factor to schoolchildren, that they will be most appreciative of the course, and will be very serious and responsible in giving ratings and making comments. Consider allowing students

Celebrities support an Open Day.

organizations) and fund raising drives for new equipment can be attempted concurrently. One such open day in Leicestershire in 1982 had several thousand attenders, attracted regional TV, and raised enough money to buy bicycle ergometers and cardiometry equipment. Public interest in fitness should not be underestimated, and with careful planning can work for you.

6. Good teaching tips

It is easy to become over-enthusiastic and give the impression that a health-related fitness course will be a storming success. There can be some real problems also. The following are notes of caution to prevent diffculties at the outset:

– Don't make classes over academic. A school fitness class should not be conducted as though it was a pilot class for medical school. Advanced academics, especially in areas such as anatomy and physiology, might alienate from the programme the very pupils who probably need health-related fitness concepts the most. Preparation of classes should focus on promoting enjoyable, experiential learning. Factual information should only be used as a relevant foundation to fitness skills and problem-solving, not as an end in itself.

– Fitness testing can easily be abused (see Chapters 15 and 16). Keep it in perspective. Remember that there is a lot of evidence to show that health-related fitness levels are largely genetically determined. A cardiovascular fitness score that is low compared to one's peers may represent a peak of training to the individual who inherited a relatively inefficient cardiovascular system. We cannot all be a Sebastion Coe. *Activity* levels matter more than fitness scores. The ultimate goal is not necessarily the highest fitness score, but lifelong physical activity. Also there is little point in assessing fitness if the backup service or advice is not available for students to succesfully make fitness changes.

to do this anonymously. At the very worst, problems that could hurt the programme will be highlighted, and conversely, the chances are high that some very impressive data will be collected to support your statements of the success of the course.

Whenever a new programme goes well, it is also worth putting the success into print. This can range from the local newspaper to professional journals such as the *BJPE.* The media can be a very powerful agent in promoting a good course, and local reporters can be valuable allies to your efforts. It can be very worthwhile to invite the press to see your programme first hand and write it up into the local news. A word of caution however: some journalists are prone to sensationalizing their material and care should be taken to check that sound fitness and exercise messages are transmitted. Many schools hold an annual open day, where it is traditional to have sports displays. Why not give the open day a health-related fitness flavour? Many outside agencies would probably assist with displays (e.g. regional Sports Council, H.E.C., fitness

– Physical fitness is *not* health. Do not bring disrepute to physical fitness by mistaking it for freedom from illness. The unfortunate death of Jim Fixx illustrates this point, and the fact is that however enthusiastic we are, physical activity can only contribute to health, and enhance our chances of remaining healthy. It cannot guarantee it.

– Focus on individual people's needs, rather than the masses. The aim of our programme should be to assist our students in improving their quality of life. What might be an ideal activity for most, may be repulsive to a few. As far as possible, try to increase width in physical activity programme opportunities.

– Always be *sympathetic* and *empathetic*. There is a high chance of embarrassment for some students in many fitness situations, and these student's fitness needs are usually the greatest. Therefore, when conducting tests for aspects of fitness such as body fatness, privacy in testing and confidentiality of results should be the norm. Also, be aware of factors such as recent family bereavements when teaching aspects such as coronary heart disease risks. Insensitivity to problems such as this does much to perpetuate an uncaring P.E. stereotype.

– Finally, endeavour to be a good model. Although it is not suggested that teachers should become 'perfect people', it is vital to consider the example you set. Think of the impression given by an enthusiastic fitness advocate who never exercises, and is obviously out of shape. Consider the impact of a teacher who talks of coronary risk factors, but is seen to smoke. The 'hidden curriculum' could completely negate the ostensible one.

Extending Provision

It will be very surprising if a well planned health-related fitness programme does not bring rewards and success to its promoters. As success increases, there are various ways to expand the provision. Extra curricular opportunities can be increased for lifetime activities such as cycling, rambling, or swimming. Sports clubs can be extended to provide for all levels of ability, and more 'graded' intramural type competitions organised, and school teams can be 'linked up' with local community teams. A need for extra remedial provision might also emerge, to help those students whose poor coordination, overfatness, or lack of muscle fitness has become a major personal problem (see Chapter 5). This added remedial provision could either be extra curricular, timetabled (if possible), or both.

Try to make school physical activity a good preparation for post school years. Visits to local sports clubs, recreation centres, fitness clubs etc., can be of great value in promoting awareness of opportunity. Many centres may be prepared to offer students financial concessions if they are publicised in return. Feedback from student participants in and out of school programmes can also help raise awareness of good consumer skills. Which centre gives the best value? Which gives the most tuition? These and many other questions are important in maximising long-term student participation – which is one of the main goals of any health-related fitness programme.

A final concluding comment is called for. The 1980's have seen the emergence of significant and positive trends related to curriculum development in physical education. There has been a real concern that our programmes should be totally committed to ALL our students, regardless of their abilities, and that a fundamental purpose of physical education is to involve more of our students in lifetime physical activity. In the area of sports and games (Thorpe & Bunker, 1982) an 'understanding' approach has been advocated, designed to bring relevance to more students. There has also been great concern about bridging the gap between school and community involvement in sports (Stevens, 1985; Wade, 1983, physical education for life after school (Fox, 1983a) and for leisure in order to increase participation (B.J.P.E., 1985; Laventure, 1985). In this respect, the Sports Council has extended its boundaries to include more recreative, leisure and fitness orientated activities, and has targeted youth and early adulthood as a special needs group. Also the Health Education Council has actively sought links with the P.E. profession in an effort to promote healthy lifestyles.

The health-related fitness movement represents a vital part of this overall trend towards involving people in exercise, sport, and lifetime recreation. It attempts to provide a total fitness preparation for life, so that individuals emerge from their education as knowledgeable, experienced, discriminating, and above all *independant* fitness consumers. We are pleased to see that the idea of educating for physical fitness is rapidly establishing itself within the profession. Health-related fitness is here to stay, and we wish success to all who take on the challenge.

References
ALMOND, L., (1983). A rationale for health-related fitness in schools. *Bulletin of Physical Education*, Vol. 19 (2).
BAILEY, K. (1985). Health-related fitness course. *British Journal of Physical Education*, Vol. 16 (6).
British Journal of Physical Education, Vol. 16 (3), 1985. (Special issue of outdoor education).
CORBIN, C. B., & LINDSEY, R., (1983). *Fitness for life.* Glenview, Illinois: Scott, Foresman.
FOX, K. R. (1983a). Physical life skills: Further thoughts on health-related fitness. *British Journal of Physical Education.* Vol. 14 (3).
FOX, K. R. (1983b). Teaching physical life skills: Practical ideas on health-related fitness. *British Journal of Physical Education*, Vol. 14 (5).
LAVENTURE, R., (1985). Promoting an active life-style: A model for curriculum change. *British Journal of Physical Education*, Vol. 16 (4).
SLAVA, S., LAURIE, D. R., & CORBIN, C. B., (1984). Long-term effects of a conceptual physical education programme. *Research Quarterly for Exercise and Sport.* Vol. 55 (2).
STEVENS, J. E. R., (1985). Developing post-school youth participation in sport and recreation. *British Journal of Physical Education,* Vol. 16 (4).

THORPE, R., & BUNKER, D., (1982). A model for the teaching of games in secondary schools. *Bulletin of Physical Education.* Vol. 19 (1).
WADE, A., (1982). Substance and the shadow. *British Journal of Physical Education*, Vol. 13 (1).

This chapter first appeared in the *British Journal of Physical Education*, 1986, Vol. 17 (2).

Chapter Eleven

Student-Centred Physical Education

Ken Fox & Jim Whitehead

I: The Rationale

Physical education has traditionally centred around the teaching of sports. Student involvement in the variety of sporting activities that physical educators have offered has been seen to be a good idea for a number of reasons. Amongst the notable benefits have been: character-building, social competence, aesthetic awareness, fitness and motor skill development. *Which* of this array of benefits is given priority in the physical education programme at any one time, is primarily dependent on variables such as school ethos, teacher bias, headmaster bias, and whichever justification of P.E. seems fashionable at the time.

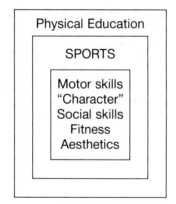

Figure 1. The traditional model.

Referring to Figure 1, we have tended to look upon our job as teaching sports in the hope that the process, in a kind of mixing bowl fashion, has helped to create desirable qualities in our students. We didn't design the system. It is more a result of our culture and tradition than planning, and does not necessarily provide us with the best educational tools.

However, as a profession, we have done our best to mould and shape the traditional sports model to ensure that students have gained from their experiences and involvement. As a result

of decades of practice there have been undoubted improvements and successes, but this sports model is fraught with dangers, not least of which is when the dog bites the hand of the master and becomes the master itself. In too many schools, sports are still taught as an end in themselves, *often* as a means of prestige and *frequently* at the expense of a large percentage of the student core.

A more logical, efficient and relevant framework on which to work would be centred on the student in an attempt to fulfil his/her needs in society. If we are to look at broad educational principles we should be doing our utmost to help our students be best prepared for adult life. The service that *physical* education has to offer is concerned with involvement of students in large scale *physical* activity. If we are to justify our service as being essential, we must begin by offering to the student that which is unique to physical education and base our programmes around this. Development of social skills, aesthetic awareness, are not exclusive to physical education and many areas in the curriculum, such as drama or art, can be more effective. We must ensure that we deal successfully with those qualities that are the sole concern of P.E. and essential to the student before we look to providing the added advantages. The benefits that physical activity offers which are *unique* and *essential* to all students in helping them lead a full and healthy adulthood are as follows:–

1. It is the means by which we learn to create and control our body movements. Motor competence in the areas of co-ordination, agility, and balance, for example, are important to everybody.
2. It is the way that we keep physically fit. Exercise is vital to looking good, feeling good, and protecting ourselves against "modern" diseases (Fentem and Bassey, 1977.)

In addition, although not essential, physical

activity is an excellent medium for leisure, relaxation and enjoyment, all of which in turn can affect our health, fitness status and feelings of well-being.

It is at this point that the model in Figure 1 begins to disintegrate. Motor development and lifetime fitness can easily be achieved *without* involvement in organised sports. Evidence points out that 90% of total motor development takes place through play before the age of 12 when little organised sports teaching has taken place (Corbin, 1976). Adults, when choosing activity to keep fit or as a leisure pursuit, walk, cycle, swim, fish, or jog in much greater numbers than those taking part in traditional sports (Sports Council, 1982). *It comes as a shock to many involved in the physical education profession that sports are NOT the esssential elements of physical education.* A large percentage of our adult population manage to lead a healthy and happy life despite their involvement with sports being restricted to a fleeting and probably unsuccessful encounter during school days. If the sports model continues as our system, we risk being accused of providing a non-essential service, and our existence on the curriculum will be rightfully threatened.

We need to design our service around our students' needs (Figure 2). The model begins with the student. Our clients (1) are students, whether they are youngsters, adolescents or adults. The essential service (2) that we offer, we have termed physical education. The desirable qualities (3) which we claim we can enhance uniquely through physical education might be called motor or movement competence and achievement of lifetime fitness. In the case of motor competence, we analyse the skills (4) that are necessary, such as hand-eye co-ordination, limb co-ordination, balance or agility. We then use the medium of physical activity (5) to develop the skills. The tool (6) chosen might be a sport such as basketball, but it may be more suitable to allow free play or use a specific practice or dance, or gymnastics.

Health-related fitness

The main purpose of this paper is to discuss

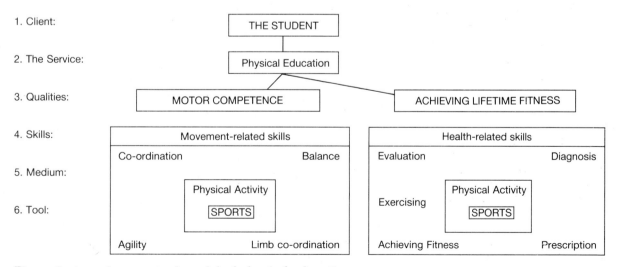

Figure 2. A student-centred model of physical education.

the place of lifetime fitness or health-related fitness concepts in the physical education programme, and in particular their practical application in one Leicestershire Upper School. Health-related fitness teaching is gaining momentum and we are concerned that it does not become yet another additive to the mixing bowl or merely an extra responsibility tagged onto our provsision.

> The teaching of lifetime fitness is the second *fundamental element* that physical education has to offer. We should endeavour to design our system accordingly.

Returning to the model (Figure 2), to help our students achieve lifetime fitness we need to teach them health-related skills. In order to have a lasting effect on the state of health and fitness of our students we should develop cognitive as well as behavioural skills. Unlike motor competence, which tends to have a high degree of retention once acquired, you cannot store fitness, and achieving lifetime fitness is as much to do with a healthy attitude as a healthy body. Students must be in a position to solve their own fitness problems independently. In order to do this they must have the knowledge and skills of evaluating the different parts of fitness and understand which parts are most important. They must know how to exercise effectively and safely, be aware of the problems caused by lack of physical activity (hypokinetic disease[1]), and also understand the value that different sports and activities have on fitness. For example, is yoga beneficial to cardiovascular health, or is involvement in popmobility successful in body fat reduction? Students should also recognise the problems of continuing their involvement in physical activity after leaving school, such as expense or

transport difficulties. Finally, with the acquired knowledge, attitude and skills we hope that all our students will, for a variety of personal benefits, wish to be involved in some form of activity, be it football, jogging, home exercise or outdoor pursuits.

It is clear then that within this framework the real skills of the physical education teacher lie in using whatever means are at his/her disposal to enhance student attitudes towards physical activity. Understanding and enjoyment are fundamental. Sport skill acquisition becomes secondary but all are important if we want students to be enlightened, confident, and motivated to chose physical activity as part of their lifestyle.

Responsibility

So far in this paper we have concerned ourselves with fitness in terms of physical activity, as this is unique to our traditional understanding of 'physical education'. It soon becomes apparent, however, that exercise fitness is only one part of physical fitness

---

(1) 'hypokinetic disease': disease related to lack of exercise (Kraus and Raab, 1961).

(Figure 3). Diet and nutrition, and stress and relaxation concepts deserve consideration as well, as they are very closely interlinked with physical activity, (see chapters 7, 8 and 9). For example, body fatness is a result of calorie intake as well as calorie expenditure through exercise. The stress response is largely a physiological preparation for extreme physical activity, with the result that physical activity is an extremely effective way to alleviate the symptoms of stress. Our definition of physical fitness *has* to include these factors, and if we operate under the title of "physical educator" we must pass on the skills of eating well and managing stress in addition to our traditional involvement with exercise. How far the "physical education" department will take on these responsibilities will also depend on liaison with other departments, such as home economics and drama.

Concern about health and fitness is growing amongst the general public but the knowledge and skills of health-related fitness are sadly lacking. A large percentage of the adult population still believe that fitness is a quality which can only be acquired through "being good at sport". If we restrict our service in physical education to the teaching of sports we go a long way to downgrading the quality of lives of a large proportion of those who pass through our hands. A student who has the knowledge, skills, confidence and motivation to be physically active and fit for life should be our end product.

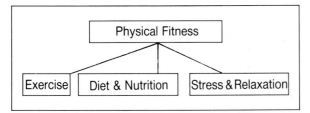

Figure 3. Physical Fitness

II: The Application

Having taken the liberty of presenting a framework in which we believe the teaching of health-related fitness should be developed, we move to the more difficult task of putting theory into practice. Changing programmes over-night would be both unrealistic and counterproductive but with a student-centred model as a theoretical base it is possible to make alterations and additions to our provision so that we can better satisfy our students needs (see also chapter 10).

This part of the chapter deals with the teaching of lifetime fitness concepts at Rawlins Upper School and Community College, Leicestershire. The programme described is compulsory for 4th and 5th year co-ed students and is a result of over five years of change and adaptation. We regard it as still being in the early stages.

For simplicity, we will describe the two main components separately:

1. The Theory Component

A fundamental aim is to allow our students to make *intelligent* decisions about their lifestyles. Intelligent decisions are *informed* decisions and so a factual element to the course was essential. Information about diet, smoking, ischaemic heart disease, or back pain, can directly alter attitudes and behaviour. Fifth year girls will jog if they fully understand the health benefits but are unlikely to entertain cross-country running. More importantly, there is a greater chance that they will continue to jog after leaving school. Information explaining that your diet of doughnuts and coke can affect your powers of concentration or make you diabetic may alter your eating habits. In some cases information *is* effective in changing habit.

Knowledge and understanding, however, are not the total answer. As we have mentioned earlier there are also definite skills which we need to develop in students (see Figure 4).

SOLVING OUR OWN FITNESS PROBLEMS
1. *Evaluating* – measuring the different components of fitness, including diet and stress levels.
2. *Diagnosis* – recognising which components require attention.
3. *Prescription* – deciding the appropriate course of action.
4. *Taking action* – taking exercise, modifying diet and relaxing accordingly.

Figure 4. The skills of physical fitness.

For example an evaluation of body composition might reveal large skinfold thickness. The diagnosis follows that the student's body fat percentage is too high because calorie balance is out. The prescription requires the student to exercise more and cut down certain high calorie foods such as fats. Taking the right course of action requires that the student is able to recognise and take up the sort of exercise that will use up a lot of calories in addition to restricting eating the type of foods high in fats. Skills are essential if the student is to work through this series of informed decisions, independently, so that he/she can solve their individual fitness problems. A combination of knowledge, understanding and skills such as these will vastly increase the chances of our students taking up healthy lifestyles.

A more detailed outline of this theory content is shown in Table 2. It is fair to say that we have adopted a holistic definition of physical fitness and try to work very closely with individuals and their lifestyle patterns.

Throughout the 4th and 5th year at regular intervals, students measure their height, weight, and triceps skinfold and record them on personalised 'Record of Growth' cards. This has two real advantages. Firstly, students take great interest in their changing body shape through adolescence and with the help of instruction, understand the concept of body composition. Secondly, it allows us to recognise quickly any abnormal trends in developments such as a tendency to large body fat increases or conversely to anorexia (see chapter 7). Action can then be taken by the student, with or without the help of the teacher, to reverse the trend. Also at the end of the 5th year a comprehensive look at personal lifestyle patterns, including exercise, diet and stress, helps students to understand the real problems that they are likely to face, especially as they grow older. It is hoped at this stage that students have now become much better equipped to overcome any lifestyle problems.

We decided to teach this theory component in a classroom/laboratory setting and have acquired a room (from the music department) which is

Aspects	Application	Provision
How to Exercise (Experiential learning)	Compulsory	Gymnasium based course Weight training
Activities for fitness and leisure	Optional	Jogging Aerobics Popmobility Swimming, Dance Cycling etc.
Sports for fitness and leisure	Optional	Individual and team sports: Badminton Soccer etc.

Table 1.
Current Rawlins practical course.

big enough to allow for a variety of teaching methods. We fully support the experiential learning approach (Almond, 1983) and involve students in discussion, dramatised role-play, and stunts of various kinds. We have now built up a 'bank' of resources, including films, videos, slides, work sheets and pamphlets. Our thanks go to Leicestershire Health Authority for their continued help on this.

The test of the success of any service lies with client satisfaction. Through a standardised anonymous questionnaire, over 300 students have rated the course as being enjoyable, relevant to their needs, taught well, and effective in improving their attitude to their personal fitness needs. Equally important, the responses have shown us the areas where the course needs further improvement.

2. The Practical Component

A fundamental aim of our course is to encourage our students to make intelligent decisions about physical activity in their lifestyles. The practical component (i) aims to give students the experience of different ways of exercising and, (ii) offers a variety of activities and sports which they might wish to use as a means of improving and maintaining fitness, relaxing and enjoying leisure, (see Table 1).

(a) Learning how to exercise

This is a direct extension of the theory part of the course and compulsory for all students.

In the gymnasium-based course, the emphasis

4TH YEAR (age 14/15)	Unit 1	*Physical Fitness – Exercise* The importance of exercise and physical activity, cardiovascular fitness, strength, and muscular endurance, flexibility and body composition – their importance, their measurement and how to achieve and maintain them. How to exercise effectively and safely.	
	Unit 2	*Accidents, First Aid, Safety* How to deal with motor vehicle, domestic, sports and everyday accidents, and their preventions.	
5TH YEAR (age 15/16)	Unit 3	*Lifestyle Management 1* Preventive medicine. Cardiovascular illness and fitness. Diet and nutrition, weight control. Stress management and relaxation. Smoking and drug abuse.	
	Unit 4	*Lifestyle Management 2* Lifestyle problem solving – an appraisal of individual lifestyle patterns. Links with the community, sports clubs and leisure facilities.	
ON-GOING		Individual Record Cards of height, weight, skinfold measurement and fitness evaluations.	

Each unit is presented as a 5-week block (in cycle with Careers and R.E.) with two 50 minute periods per week. All lessons are now timetabled in our own fitness laboratory which has ample lockable storage space for teaching materials and fitness evaluation equipment. All staffing is by full-time PE teachers.

Table 2.
A theory component for health-related fitness.

is on different exercise programmes. Included are lessons on how to begin jogging, achieving fitness through different types of circuits, experiencing 'aerobics', flexibility exercises, and effective body fat reduction. Enjoyment is a prime consideration in tempering the somewhat purposeful elements of this part of the course. Fun activities such as "new" games, and "Its a Knockout" are used to help create a conducive and endearing atmosphere, particularly as this is often the first practical course for the students.

Weight training (as opposed to weightlifting) is also experienced by students. With the use of the principles of overload and progression, employing free weights and other apparatus such as exercise cycles, we explain improvements in strength and muscular endurance. The value of the activity for producing a 'toned' figure or physique is explained. There have been some unfortunate notions about weight-training. When the mythology of muscle boundness and bulging muscles for girls is exposed as being untrue, the activity becomes very popular – particularly with girls who are keen on improving their figure and those boys who have found little success in the rough and tumble of most 'traditional' sports (Whitehead & Biddle, 1981; see chapter 5).

(b) *Activities and sports for fitness and leisure*
Besides providing exercise experience we have a duty to offer different activities and sports as tools for achievement of fitness, enjoyment and relaxation, and worthy use of leisure time. All are vital to overall health-related fitness. In this category of activities, we would include non-competitive, individually based pastimes, such as popmobility, jogging, aerobics, swimming, dance, and cycling. Students who chose to be involved in this type of option may have found little success in highly skilled or contact activities, such as hockey or rugby, or may simply be more interested in the aesthetic and

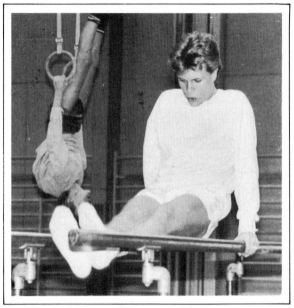

intrinsic qualities of this type of activity.

A wide range of traditional sports is also offered for those students who enjoy the social setting of team games, the achievement of racquet and ball skills, or merely the challenge of competing against others.

The importance here is enjoyment and involvement in physical activity and if we are to satisfy a wide range of needs, we must provide a variety of options.

Changing Teaching Styles
Probably more important than our system of practical activities is the adoption of a student-centred teaching style that is consistent throughout our department. We attempt to be more sensitive to our students' feelings and problems and look at them as individuals with differing needs, rather than as groups. We also try to appreciate their worth as human beings having an equal right to our expertise and attention, whatever their ability, disposition and aptitude.

The provision of practical opportunities is always limited by the facilities we inherit, but our teaching can become more effective, whatever the situation, with an understanding and humanistic approach.

Remedial Physical Education
Most secondary schools have a system of remedial help for those students who have poor reading and writing skills. Literacy, it seems, is

a priority skill for adult life. Similarly our teaching of health-related fitness has brought to light examples of students who are desperate for remedial *physical* help if they are to grow to be happy and healthy adults. Adolescence is a time when youngsters are obsessed with their physical self. Physical prowess, in particular for boys, and body image in general, tend to be yardsticks of normality. For some students, their physical problems, or at least their perceptions of them, are highest amongst their sources of worry and depression and we suggest are closely related to their low levels of self-esteem. The obese girl who finds sports embarrassing and so hates herself as a result, or the weak or unco-ordinated boy who is intimidated by his peers, could benefit greatly from remedial physical help. The girl requires dietary help and a personalised exercise programme whereas the boy may need extra time working with a weight training group of similar ability. We have a duty to provide this extra help for the students who need it. We feel that a major failure of our health-related fitness provision at Rawlins so far has been our inability to secure sufficient curriculum time to tackle the variety of remedial problems that we discover. (Our help at Rawlins so far is primarily restricted to extra-curricular time and one period per week on the timetable!).

Exceptional students need exceptional provision. Those who are exceptionally gifted are often able to satisfy their needs out of school. Those who have exceptional physical *problems* are far less likely to find help without our care.

In addition, we regard those adults in the community who have passed through the system without being exposed to our health-related fitness programme as requiring *remedial* physical education. In fact their lack of knowledge, questioning and feelings that their school P.E. experiences have done little to help them through their adult fitness difficulties has

provided us with some of the momentum for developing our health-related fitness teaching. Our community college courses for adults cover 'Fitness for Lifetime Health', Yoga, Badminton, Popmobility and many other activities, including a fitness evaluation and exercise prescription service. We are also trying to finance a community fitness facility including a multi-station weights machine. Sadly our adult population is *not* a captive audience and we have to rely upon that small percentage who are motivated volunteers.

Final remarks

This chapter has presented the need to change from a sports-based to a student-based model. Central to the argument is the recognition that our clients are students with individual needs and an equal worth as human beings. We must demonstrate that we can provide an irrefutably essential service that helps to satisfy our client's needs in society. If we do not, we risk our existence in a changing curriculum.

In consideration of student needs, physical education professionals must have a sound scientific training on the *application* of exercise physiology, anatomy, and nutrition. They must be in the business of creating healthy attitudes as well as fit bodies and therefore understand the psychological principles involved. In short, they must be in a position to answer the public's questions and help solve their problems in achieving an active and healthy life.

The media are presently doing more to physically educate the nation than the physical education profession. In the meantime, inexperienced, unqualified, and potentially dangerous personnel are selling the public the service which should be our responsibility. As long as we continue to produce young teachers who know more about cricket than coronary heart disease, and who value their first team football results more than the quality of life of their students, we cannot honestly claim full right to the title of 'physical educator'.

References
ALMOND, L. (1983). Health-Related Fitness. *British Journal of Physical Education,* Vol. 14 (2).
CORBIN, C. B. (1976). *Becoming Physically Educated in the Elementary School.* Lea & Febiger: Philadelphia.
CORBIN, C. B. and LINDSEY, R. (1985). *Concepts in Physical Fitness.* Dubuque, Iowa: Wm. C. Brown Co. (5th edn.).
FENTEM, P. M., and BASSEY, E. J. (1977). *The Case for Exercise.* Research Working Paper No. 8. London, The Sports Council.
KRAUS, H., AND RAAB (1961). *Hypokinetic Disease.* Illinois: Charles C. Thomas.
THE SPORTS COUNCIL (1982). *Sport in the Community: The Next Ten Years.* London: The Sports Council.
WHITEHEAD, J. R. and BIDDLE, S. J. H. (1981). Slimline Weightlifting. *British Journal of Physical Education,* Vol. 12 (3).

This chapter first appeared in the *Bulletin of Physical Education,* 1983, Vol. 19 (2), and is re-printed with permission.

Chapter Twelve

Health-Related Fitness for Young Children

Robert P. Pangrazi

One of the current areas of concern today is the lack of physical fitness among children. In many instances, the school environment is not providing enough time and organized activity to develop an adequate level of fitness among its youth. Schools may be shortchanging youth in the area of health and 'wellness' by refusing to offer physical education programmes which offer emphasis and organization for health-related fitness development.

Is Physical Fitness Necessary for Children?

This question asked on a regular basis, usually by disbelievers who visualise children as highly active beings. There are a number of ways to examine the question and to offer justification for physical fitness programming. The first is to look at youngsters and ask a question in return. Are they healthy? It appears that, in many cases, today's children are not healthy and have a strong need for physical fitness activity. Allied to this problem is the inactivity of youngsters during the school day. Many adults observe children during recess and assume they are extremely active. Apparently, this is not the case. In a study by Gilliam et. al. (1982), it was found that children do not voluntarily engage in high intensity activity. High intensity activity by definition occurs when the heart elevates to at least 60% of its maximum. The heart rate of children was monitored to see how mush time, during a 12 hour period, was spent in high intensity activity. Less than two percent of the time was spent by children in high intensity activity while 80 percent of the time was spent in low intensity. Obviously, children are not receiving enough fitness enhancing activity during play experiences to develop an adequate level of health-related fitness. In addition to this finding, the researchers also found that girls were even less active than boys.

In the study above, it was also shown that school decreases the physical activity patterns of children. When compared to summer, children's activity patterns decreased during the school year. Another interesting finding showed that if girls are given the opportunity, they will increase their activity levels to comparable or above most moderately active boys. This seems to illustrate two obvious points: fitness does not occur through unorganized recess periods and fitness is suitable for all children. This is a key point; health-related physical fitness improvement can be accomplished by all, including boys, girls, handicapped, and obese children. This contrasts with sport skills which demand a certain amount of inherent skill. Health-related physical fitness is an easy commodity to sell children if it is based on success and self-improvement.

Exercise and Health Maintenance

An area of concern dealing with children's health is in the area of heart disease (see Chapter 3). It has long been thought that heart disease is of geriatric origin and only manifests itself in older adults. In a study by Glass (1973),

youngsters in Iowa state schools were examined over a two year period. Of these students, 70% had risk factors for coronary heart disease, 7% had extremely high cholesterol levels, a large precentage had high blood pressure, and at least 12% were obese. The lifestyles of children need to be changed before their 8th birthday. Prior to this time, dietary and exercise patterns are relatively easy to change, but become increasing more difficult to change as the youngster matures. In examining the developmental history of arteriosclerosis in humans, Dr. Kenneth Rose (1973), identified the first signs of heart disease appearing around the age of 2. The good news is that he also stated that the disease process is reversible until the age of 19.

Wilmore and McNamara (1974) and Gilliam et.al. (1977) found that more than 50% of children tested had one or more risk factor (elevated blood pressure, cholesterol levels, or obesity). The serious part of these findings lies in the fact that it appears that children burdened with high blood pressure and/or obesity maintain these problems as they mature into adults. It is well documented that these factors are precursors to chronic heart disease in adults thereby increasing the risk of coronary heart disease early in life.

Other detractors of physical fitness experiences for children point to the fact that we have an imperfect school system. For example, they point out that physical education classes sometimes meet only once a week, actual fitness changes in children may not occur, or ask the question, "develop physical fitness for what purpose?" It is all too apparent that the schools have many weaknesses as well as strengths. To avoid teaching lifetime fitness is to avoid developing important lifestyles for adulthood. Youngsters must begin to learn that exercising daily (independently) is an important habit for a healthy lifestyle. Certainly, we teach our young how to brush their teeth at a tender

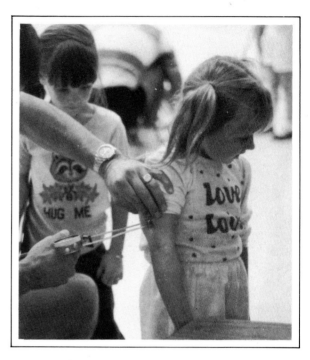

age in order to assure they will not decay. How can one justify not teaching children to take a few minutes each day to assure that one's total health will not decay? The justification for teaching many different ways to retain fitness (even if only one day per week) is that it suggests that the school values personal health and views exercise as an important habit to be done on a regular basis.

To summarize: youth as a whole are not overly healthy. Most adults assume that if a youngster is moving, playing, and not complaining, they are healthy. The evidence points in a contrary direction. Youth are afflicted by symptoms of heart disease and it appears that unhealthy children grow into unhealthy adults. Certainly, this is not a legacy we want to leave our children. It is important to develop the patterns of life now so that children can enter adulthood with the odds for a healthy lifespan in their favour.

Fitness Programming

A balanced physical fitness programme should offer the following to its participants:

a. Develop an understanding that maintenance of lifetime physical fitness is the responsibility of each student.
b. Provide an understanding of how fitness is

developed.

c. Develop cognition of the importance of fitness as a part of 'wellness'.

d. Provide a developmental fitness programme that is activity based and a part of each physical education lesson.

To develop fitness in any individual a few basic principles must be adhered to in order to assure that the physical demands are prescribed in a manner which assures fitness improvement in a safe manner. The following points are described with brevity. For greater detail see Corbin and Lindsey (1985). **FIT** is an acronym which is useful for the purpose of remembering the rules for fitness prescription (see Chapter 4). **(F)**requency is the number of times per week fitness activities should be performed. Three times per week is the minimum. **(I)**ntensity of cardiovascular exercise can be monitored by teaching children to check their heart rate. The training rate is reached when the heart rate is elevated over 160 beats per minute and should be maintained for a miniumum of 10 minutes. **(T)**ime is the length of each exercise bout. A typical physical education period is 30 minutes in length. At least 10 minutes of the period should be devoted to activity which elevates the heart rate into the training zone as described above.

Progression is an important concept to remember when teaching fitness activities to children. The typical stereotype for physical fitness instruction has been the "daily dozen calisthenics and run a mile" approach. This defeats everything known about individualized instruction. There is tremendous variation among children in terms of physical capacity which necessitates teaching to these differences. One of the most effective ways of turning children off exercise for a lifetime is to ask them to do more than they are capable of performing. Therefore, keep initial demands low and gradually increase the workload. Organize activites so children do not have to start and

differing capacities. Begin the year with demands that are low so that all children experience success. The "battle may be won but the war lost" if children cultivate a negative attitude toward activity due to excessive workloads placed on them by an overenthusiastic instructor.

A variety of fitness activities should be offered children. Youngsters often tire of the same activities and the motivation to exercise is decreased when children perceive the activities to be boring. Secondly, most adults who exercise have a favourite type of exercise. It is reasonable to think that children have similar likes and dislikes and should be taught that there are many "paths to fitness" and that no single type of exercise is best for all people. Teach children a number of ways of exercising their way to fitness for life and how to modify each way to assure that fitness benefits will accrue.

Aerobic Capacity

Aerobic capacity, all other factors being equal, determines the magnitude of an individual's performance in endurance orientated activities. Since a major share of health-related physical fitness depends on cardiovascular fitness, it is important to understand the capabilities and limitations of children in this area.

Aerobic power is closely related to lean body mass, which explains why obese children and girls are often at a disadvantage in endurance activities. Girls tend to show an increase in body fat and a decrease in lean body weight as they mature which causes a gradual decrease in aerobic capacity when values are adjusted by body weight (Bar-Or, 1983).

A point often raised by individuals who question endurance activities for children is whether training actually improves their aerobic capacity. Research results differ in that some studies have shown a significant increase while others have reported no improvement. It appears that, particularly in children under 10 years of age, aerobic power does not increase with training even though running performance improves. The reason for the improvement in performance is speculation. However, it is thought that children may become more efficient mechanically or may improve in anaerobic metabolism. Regardless of this issue, the fact remains that children should participate in aerobic activites in order to develop meaningful fitness habits and an understanding that aerobic exercise is the cornerstone of a lifelong fitness programme.

Even though children exhibit a relatively high oxygen uptake, they do not perform up to this level because they are not economical in running or walking activities. An 8 year old child running at 180 m per minute is operating at 90% of maximum aerobic power, while a 16 year old running at the same rate is only at 75% of maximum. This explains why children should *not* be expected to perform workloads

similar to adolescents, particularly over long distances. Youngsters can run long distances at a slow speed which usually means they should not be pushed by demanding adults. Encouragement yes, demands no!

Children are blessed in that they perceive activity to be easier that do adults exercising at a similar level. The Rating of Perceived Exertion was administered at different percentages of maximal heart rate (Bar-Or, 1977) and revealed that children perceive exercise to be less strenuous than adults. The reason for this is unknown, however much research has documented the rapid recovery rate of children and that exercise does not demand as much of children as it does of adults. The point of application for teachers is that they should not determine workloads for children based upon their perceptions of exercise difficulty. For example, if a teacher is not in a well-trained state, he or she might perceive the mile run to be next to impossible. Obviously, this would not be the case for the majority of children.

Effective fitness instruction would assure taking advantage of children's rapid recovery rate. Aerobic activity can be interspersed with restful stretching and nonlocomotor movements to extend the amount of time effectively devoted to physical fitness development. It should be clear that interval training is well-suited to the young child with bouts of intense activity being alternated with less demanding exercise.

Obesity and Physical Activity

Not only does obesity affect the attractiveness of children, it takes a great toll on their aerobic power because of the greater metabolic cost of exercise. Obese children must perform at a higher percentage of their maximal oxygen uptake. To compound the problem, their maximal uptake values are often lower than those of lean children. This gives them less reserve and makes them perceive higher exertion when performing a task. These manifestations combine to offer teachers a child "who doesn't enjoy running"

Teachers must understand that the obese child is working harder than a normal weight youngster. Workloads must be adjusted accordingly. All children *do not* have to do the same amount of exercise. Just as one would not expect kindergarten children to perform the same workloads as 10 year olds, it is unreasonable to expect obese children to be capable of workloads similar to lean, ectomorphic youngsters.

Many adults believe that diet is the factor dictating whether children will become obese. Research doesn't support the thesis that obese children ingest more calories than normal weight children. The area in which normal and overweight children differ dramatically is in the area of physical activity. As an example, a study of 13 year old girls who were obese showed they ate less but also exercised two-thirds less (in total time) than normal weight girls (Johnson, et.al. 1956). Unfortunately, many obese children have a decreased tendency for physical activity. As their weight increases, the impulse for physical exertion further decreases and thus starts a negative cycle. It is important for teachers to realize that it will take some exceptionally sensitive teaching to reach the obese youngster. However, if the child is further turned off exercise by physical education instruction, the opportunity to conquer a lifetime of obesity will most likely be lost (see Chapter 7).

Suggested Cardiovascular Fitness Activities
1. Random Jogging Programme: This is one of the easiest approaches which can be administered on a school-wide basis. Children are released from class to run with a friend. Allow them to select a friend of equal ability and randomly jog throughout the playground area. The teacher can time the duration of the session and signal when students are to return to the classroom. If desired, a two-minute cool-down period of walking can be allowed. Start the programme by asking youngsters to jog/walk for 4 minutes. Each week the time can be increased by one minute until students are jogging for 10 to 12 minutes. Students can walk if necessary, but are encouraged to avoid just standing. Pairing with a friend usually means that students of equal ability will be together and will be able to chat and enjoy the activity.
2. Set up a number of exercise trails on the playground. Trails should be of differing lengths so students can increase their workload as their fitness levels improve. Encourage them to keep track of their "mileage" by recording it on a class chart.
3. Move across the countryside by posting a map in the classroom. Each day, the mileage of each student is added together and the distance plotted on the map. This tends to bring the class together for a common cause and all can feel as though they are making a meaningful contribution.
4. Set up a large clock in the playground area with a second hand so students can learn to monitor their heart rate. Encourage them to maintain the training heart rate for 5 to 10 minutes prior to participation in break-time activities. Typical break-time activities are usually characterized by short bouts of activity followed by long bouts of rest. Encourage participation in activites which demand longer bouts of activity, i.e., soccer, team handball, and tag games.
5. Develop a fitness circuit utilizing playground equipment. Some playgrounds have pull-up bars, monkey bars, climbing apparatus and parallel bars. Organize a red, white, and blue circuit whereby each colour indicates a greater workload. Develop the circuit so youngsters have to run after each strength development exercise.
6. Develop an after-school fitness club. A great deal of time and energy is spent on developing

sports programmes for children even though it is well documented that a large majority of students do not possess the genetic traits to be outstanding athletes. This is the attractiveness of a fitness club; every student, regardless of inherited ability, can improve his/her level of physical fitness. The club should focus on fitness gains and teach a large number of aerobic activities, i.e., bicycling, hiking, power walking, cross-country running, and rope jumping. Students can learn to get fit in order to play sports which contrasts with the typical pattern of playing sports with the hope (usually unrealized) of developing physical fitness.

7. Conduct a health-related physical fitness day. This designated day could be part of a total 'wellness' workshop. Invite experts in the area of drug and substance abuse, alcohol awareness, stress reduction and nutrition to set up displays and offer presentations to students.

As part of the presentation, physical fitness testing and interpretation of results should be conducted. The American Alliance of Health, Physical Education, Recreation, and Dance (1985) recommends, and has established norms for, the following test items:

 a. One mile run/walk (measures cardiovascular fitness)
 b. Sit-ups (measures abdominal strength/ endurance)
 c. Sit and Reach (evaluates lower-back and hamstring flexibility)
 d. Skinfold measurement (body composition)

The results of the test can be sent home to parents along with other evaluated items such as hearing, vision, blood pressure, and a dental inspection. This "wellness profile" can often be the source of a strong public relations programme and communicate potential health problems of students to parents.

8. As part of the physical education programme, establish a physical fitness self-testing programme which teaches students how to evaluate their personal fitness. For example, if

the test items above were used, students would learn how to test cardiovascular fitness, abdominal strength/endurance, lower-back and hamstring flexibility, and to use skin calipers in evaluating body composition. Norms can be posted so students can see how fit they are compared to other students their age (see chapters 15 and 16).

Fitness for a Lifetime

The key for a healthy lifestyle is developed around the word *moderation*. To date, there is no evidence to show that children are harmed by exercise when it is offered in moderation. A guiding principle is to make sure children are allowed the opportunity to make decisions about their capabilities. Too often instructors "do something" to children without allowing the youngster input. This process does little to help the child understand their strengths and weaknesses and may cause a great deal of frustration. The days of a "daily dozen calisthenics and run a mile" must go the way of the dinosaur. There are many paths to fitness and each individual must be allowed the opportunity to discover the approach that works best for them. If people are expected to exercise for a lifetime, they must learn activities which they enjoy and find beneficial.

This is not to suggest that the physical fitness experiences should not be demanding. Rather, it is suggested that a youngster's feelings and self-worth should be considered at all times. Instructors must begin to consider the importance of nurturing and supporting students rather than causing embarrassment or belittling students when they find it impossible to measure up to expectations. Youngsters find it very difficult to separate the behaviour of the instructor from the content of the course. If they don't like the teacher, they probably won't like the subject matter. This necessitates that the instructor develop positive relationships with students if positive feelings toward physical fitness are going to be cultivated.

In summary, be demanding and expect youngsters to perform. Educators have long understood that people will, to some degree, live up to expectations others have of them. Certainly, students should not be misled into believing that lifetime fitness is a relatively easy process. Fitness demands hard work and self-discipline and students should understand the process clearly. On the other hand, teachers should live up to expectations students have about them; that they are fair, understand individual differences, and care about the feelings and needs of students. Those teachers who lead students to goals thought unattainable are true heroes!

References
American Alliance for Health, Physical Education, Recreation, and Dance (1985). *Health-related physical fitness test manual*. Reston , Virginia: AAHPERD.
BAR-OR, O. (1977). Age-related changes in exercise perception. In Borg, G. (Ed.) *Physical work and effort*. New York: Pergamon Press.
BAR-OR, O. (1983). *Pediatric sports medicine for the practitioner*. New York: Springer-Verlag.
CORBIN, C.B. & LINDSEY, R. (1985). *Concepts of physical fitness* (5th Ed.), Dubuque, Iowa: Wm.C. Brown.
GILLIAM, T.B., KATCH, V.L., THORLAND, W.G., and WELTMAN, A.W. (1977). Prevalence of coronary heart disease risk factors in active children, 7 to 12 years of age. *Medicine and Science in Sports*, Vol. 9(1) .
GILLIAM, T.B., MacCONNIE, S.E., GEENEN, D.L., PELLS , A.E., & Freedson, P.S. (1982). Exercise programmes for children: A way to prevent heart disease? *The Physician and Sports Medicine*, Vol. 10(9) .
GLASS, W. (1973). Coronary heart disease sessions prove vitally interesting. *California AHPER Journal*, May/June, 7.
JOHNSON, M.L., BURKE, B.S., & MAYER, J. (1956). The prevalence and incidence of obesity in a cross-section of elementary and secondary school children. *American Journal of Clinical Nutrition*, Vol. 4(3) .
ROSE, K. (1973). To keep people in health. *Journal of the American College Health Association*, Vol. 22
WILMORE, J.H. & McNAMARA, J.J. (1974). Prevalence of coronary disease risk factors in boys, 8 to 12 years of age. *Journal of Pediatrics*, Vol. 84 .

Editor's note: Readers may also be interested in Dr. Pangrazi's books on physical education for children of primary school age. They contain a great deal of excellent information on fitness activities for young children:
a) DAUER, V. P. & PANGRAZI, R. P. (1986). *Dynamic physical education for elementary school children*. Minnesota: Burgess (8th Edn).
b) PANGRAZI, R.P. & DAUER, V.P. (1986). *Lesson plans for dynamic physical education for elementary school children*. Minnesota: Burgess (4th Edn).

Chapter Thirteen

A Teaching/Learning Unit: The Example of Cardiovascular Fitness

Alan Hargreaves

Essentially, curriculum theory is scientific. It seeks to reduce 'the credibility gap' between what is intended and taught by teachers and what is actually learnt by students. The concept of a Teaching/Learning Unit has developed from the 'programmed learning' approach first introduced by Skinner, through the Behavioural Objectives Approach of the 1960's, into what is now called the 'Systems Approach'. The main development from the early models lies in the addition of two domains of learning. To Bloom's (1956) work in the Cognitive and Affective Domains, Singer and Dick (1980) have added the Psycho-motor and Social Domains (see Singer and Dick 1980 for further information).

The areas of knowledge included in the four domains can be summarised as follows:

Psycho-motor Domain: all bodily movements, whether they involve simple or complex perceptual motor skills; behaviours which can be characterised by the verb 'doing', for example, running, lifting, throwing, catching.

Cognitive Domain: knowledge of facts including recalling, analysing, resolving and making decisions. For example, does the student understand the effects of exercise upon the body?

Affective Domain: this is concerned with feelings and emotions, for example the internalised processes which include valuing and appreciating. Thus, in schools, pupils exercise because they appreciate its value and, by exercising regularly, demonstrate a commitment to fitness.

Social Domain: this is concerned with personal and social adjustments, for example getting on with people. It is concerned with sportsmanship, respect for authority and rules, good interpersonal relationships, positive self-image and a sense of humour.

Physical education would seem to be in a unique position to influence the development of young people in all four of these domains of learning. Unfortunately, what we have done in

the past is to assume that these kinds of effects are happening, and worse, assert that they are happening without sufficient evidence to support our case. The 'Systems Approach' represents an important way of trying to correct these errors. It does this by requiring the teacher to go through a series of planning stages *before* teaching the particular subject and then to carefully assess afterwards the effectiveness, or otherwise, of his/her teaching in each of the four domains. The successful application of the 'Systems Approach' requires a great deal of planning on the part of the teacher but the benefits, both to the pupils and in the quality of work which the teacher can achieve, are, potentially, enormous. The key to the whole approach is in learning to express one's teaching objectives in a specific way – that is in terms of what the *student* will be able to do at the end of the period of teaching. For

example, at the end of reading this chapter you should be able to:
 i) explain what is meant by a Teaching/Learning Unit;
ii) design a Teaching/Learning Unit.

A SPECIMEN TEACHING/LEARNING UNIT (for an 8 week programme on cardiovascular fitness).

Stage 1 — The Educational Goal

Following discussions we may agree to arrive at the following Educational Goal:

"Students should have a sound knowledge of the effect of exercise upon the body, possess the ability to design and quantify their own fitness programmes and, above all, have a positive attitude to fitness and health".

Stage 2 — Instructional Goal (designed to achieve part of our Educational Goal)

We now formulate our Instructional Goal as follows:

"Students will participate in, and complete, a health-related fitness programme for the improvement of cardiovascular efficiency".

Stage 3 — Instructional Analysis

Having identified our Instructional Goal we must now identify Terminal Objectives which the pupil must display in each of the four domains to achieve the Instructional Goal. We do this by identifying the subordinate skills necessary (see Figure 1)

Stage 4 — Entry Skills, Knowledge and Attitude of the Group

We must now identify the entry skills,

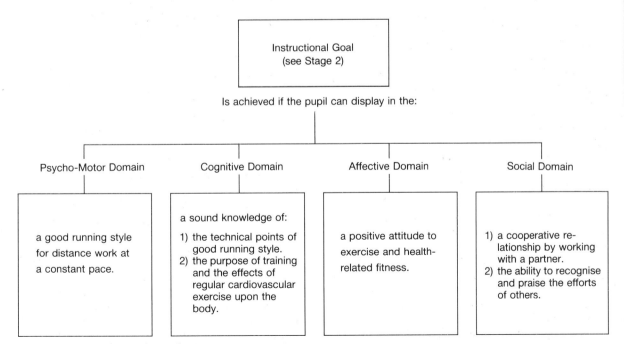

Figure 1: Instructional Analysis

knowledge and attitudes of the group by, for example:

    a) Participation in the 12 minute Run/Walk Test. This test requires pupils to cover the maximum distance possible in 12 mins, running on a 400 meter track or equivalent. The distance is recorded (see chapter 15).

    b) The completion of a short questionnaire on the effects of exercise on the body and attitudes towards health-related fitness.

The type of questions in Section (b) might include:

    i)   What happens inside your body if you run/train regularly?

    ii) Does running help to control body weight?

    iii) Do you go running, or participate in any other kind of training, in your own time?

Stage 5: Develop Performance Objectives

In Stage 5 we have to develop *Performance Objectives* in each of the four domains so that (i) we know exactly what we are looking for (ii) we can develop our series of lessons appropriately. Examples of performance objectives in each of the four domains are provided as follows.

Pupils should be able to demonstrate:

In the Psycho-motor Domain
a) A sound running style.
b) The ability to run continuously throughout the 12 min. test.
c) The ability to run at an even/constant speed.
d) A positive acceleration during the final 30 sec. of the run.
e) An improvement in the run on the final test (given good running conditions).

In the Cognitive Domain
a) A knowledge of the physiological effects of training upon various parts of the body.
b) The ability to analyse a running style and know something of pace judgement.
c) Score at least 75% on a written test about:
    (1) Technical details of the 12 min. run/walk test.
    (2) Knowledge of the effects of exercise upon the cardiovascular system.
    (3) Knowledge of good distance running, pacing and technique.

In the Affective Domain
a) That they did their best to run as well as possible during the tests (motivation factor).
b) A positive interest in what was being done.
c) An appreciation of the reasons why some people enjoy and some people not enjoy running.

In the Social Domain
a) A sense of personal achievement as a result of the programme.
b) An interest in the improvement of other members of the class, particularly his/her partner.
c) Personal encouragement towards other members of the class to do better.

Stage 6 — Criterion Reference Evaluation Instruments

Having carefully designed our Performance Objectives we must now identify how we are to assess the success or otherwise of our teaching. This is called identifying the *Criterion Reference Evaluation Instruments*. We have to identify our measuring technique in each of the four domains. Examples are given as follows:

Psycho-motor Domain
will be assessed by the 12 min. run/walk test, taking account of individual differences.

Cognitive Domain
will be assessed by a written test concerned with:
(1) Physiological effects of training.
(2) The effects of running style.
(3) Technical aspects of the 12 min. run/walk test.

Affective Domain
will be assessed by questionnaire including:
(1) Whilst you were running did you enjoy it? *A LOT / A LITTLE / NOT AT ALL.*
(2) Did you perform the test as well as possible? *YES / NEUTRAL / NO.*
(3) Did the test, and your performance, interest you? *A LOT / A LITTLE / NOT AT ALL.*
(4) Did you discuss your participation in the programme with your parents? *A LOT / A LITTLE /NOT AT ALL.*

Social Domain
will be assessed by questionnaire including:
(1) Did you personally encourage any other member of the group? *A LOT / A LITTLE / NOT AT ALL.*
(2) Were you interested in the performance of any other member of the group? *SEVERAL / ONE OR TWO / NONE.*

Stage 7 — Planning the Teaching Programme
The following programme is provided as a basis for discussion.

Session 1
i) Warming-up activities including flexibility.
ii) 12 min. run/walk test in paris (if pacing is known).
iii) Recording results.
iv) Pupils answer questionnaire concerning their attitudes towards the test and interest in fitness generally.

Session 2
i) Short discussion/video tape of the London Marathon involving discussions of the value of running.
ii) Analysis of good running technique for distance.

iii) Practice on the track for:
   a) running style
   b) even pace
   c) in pairs ½ lap running and change-overs
      (pupil runs 200 metres then walks across
      the centre of the track to receive the
      baton from the runner B).

Session 3
Discussion of the principles of training:
i)   F.I.T.: Frequency, intensity and time (Corbin
     & Lindsey, 1985).
ii) Teach pulse counting/finding.
iii) In pairs determining an even pace 400 metre
     run to raise the pulse to appropriate
     threshold.

Session 4
i) Fun run – 2-3 miles over an open
    countryside if possible.
ii) Give questionnaire on motivation/attitudes
    to this kind of running.

Session 5
i)   Individual warming-up activities.
ii) 400 metre interval training in pairs
     calculating the distance travelled in 15/20
     minutes.
iii) Discussion on (i) principles of overload and
     (ii) mental concentration during running.

Session 6
i) Cross country run/road relay on circular
    course (see follow-up strategy).
ii) Talk on the effects of exercise and the
    technical factors of the 12 min. run test.

Session 7
i) Discussion of the measurement of body
    composition and the effects of distance
    running on body fatness.
ii) retest 12 min. run/walk test (in pairs).

Session 8
i)   Discussion of pre/post run tests.
ii) Completion of questionnaires on attitudes/
     social/knowledge components.
iii) Explanation of the follow-up programme for
     the 100-up club.
iv) "The First Mile" group fun run.
v)   Planning a personal programme.

Stage 8 — Use of different types of media
In addition to the actual programme the
following kinds of media will be used to support
the programme.
i)   Notice-board specialising in cardiovascular
     fitness.
ii) Pictures and articles from magazines
     concerning fitness for a lifetime.
iii) Cuttings/articles from newspapers.
iv) Clothing and equipment for running.
v)   Display of Cooper's Chart concerning the
     relative points for different kinds of activity
     e.g. swimming, cycling, squash and
     running on the spot.
vi) Display of books on running and fitness.

vii) Lunch times and supplementary
      programmes e.g. aerobic dance.
viii) Full details of the 100-up Club for running
      (also the 10 mile swimming club etc.etc.)

Stage 9
Formal assessment by staff and others on the
effectiveness of the total programme and its
possible re-design for use with the next group
of pupils.

Conclusion
Experienced teachers will recognise from the
example of a Teaching/Learning Unit that this
approach requires time and effort in both
planning and application; they will also
recognise that a disciplined, well-conceived
framework is likely to produce greater
knowledge, participation and enthusiasm on
the part of their pupils, provide reliable
information for future programmes and, above
all, give professional satisfaction.

References
BLOOM, B. S. et al. (1956). *Taxonomy of educational objectives.*
New York: McKay.
CORBIN, C. B. & LINDSEY, R. (1985). *Concepts of physical
fitness.* Dubuque, Iowa: Wm. C. Brown (5th Edn).
SINGER, R. N. & DICK, W. (1980). *Teaching physical
education: A systems approach.* New York: Houghton Mifflin.

This chapter first appeared in Biddle, S. J. H., Dugmore, D.
and Hargreaves, A. (1981). *Health-related fitness in the school
physical education programme: Introductory concepts.* North
Staffordshire Polytechnic, Department of Geography and
Recreation Studies, and is reprinted with permission.

Section D

Issues in Health–Related Fitness

Chapter Fourteen

A Health Education Approach to Physical Education

Steve Cook

Introduction

This chapter represents something of a case study of an aspect of curriculum development in physical education attempted by an ex-Head of Physical Education whose main aim over the past four years has been to develop an effective health education programme within the school curriculum.

Despite evidence from Kane's (1974) Schools Council Inquiry that motor skills development and leisure time pursuits were the top objectives among physical education teachers, people such as Edna Haydock (1979), in her efforts to help the overweight unfit 'fat girls' at St Andrews University, have shown that for some of the most vulnerable members of the school population, the physical education programme is ineffective. She discovered that a lack of skill appears to be one of the main reasons why the inactive girl did not exercise.

Vaughan Thomas (1977) also has his doubts about the effectiveness of many physical education programmes when he says:

> "In the battle for a society with a capacity for physical activity, most of the evidence shows that HOMO SEDENTARIUS is winning. The population as a whole is less physically active and tends to be carried off as a result of physical defects arising to a large extent from a lack of exercise".

Having accepted the validity of these and many other criticisms, and armed with the resultant dissatisfaction with existing physical education programmes, my decision, to begin by developing a health education programme before modifying the physical education programme was made on three grounds:–

Firstly, although one of the main aims of the physical education programme at Malet Lambert School was to promote a healthy active lifestyle among the pupils, in practical terms it was, perhaps, too traditional and too elitist to be effective across the whole school population. It would have needed very radical changes indeed

for it to satisfy these aims with the majority of pupils.

Secondly, having consulted much of the recent health education literature, I felt that there were many important aspects of health education which could not reasonably be incorporated into a physical education programme, but which did need to be discussed with the pupils.

Thirdly, health education as a planned element of our school curriculum simply did not exist. It did seem, therefore, something of a priority to establish a comprehensive health education programme.

What we are attempting to do now is to learn from our experiences in health education and physical education so that a programme of physical education can be developed which is much more likely to influence a greater number of pupils in devising and adopting a healthy active lifestyle now and throughout their lives. This does, of course, assume a primary aim of physical education to be 'education for life' and that the promotion and development of a healthy active lifestyle among individuals, in some respects, satisfies that aim.

To this end, a small informal curriculum study group has developed at the University of Hull under the guidance of Mr Michael Mawer. Whilst this chapter may not accurately reflect the opinions of any of the group except the author, many of the ideas which I shall express are the results of discussions within the group. The starting point was the Malet Lambert School Physical Education Programme in 1979, (Figure 1).

The programme was beased on two beliefs:
(i) That post-school participation in sport was likely to be the most effective influence on an individual towards leading a healthy active lifestyle,
and (ii) That this particular structure of programme was likely to be an effective way of producing a high level of post-school participation in sport.

The programme did, in fact, prove to be very successful in influencing a large number of

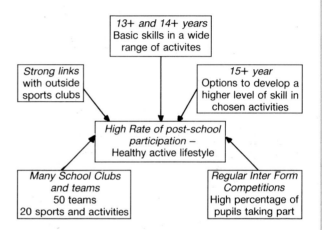

Figure 1. Malet Lambert School Physical Education Programme in 1979 (13-18 Coeducational Comprehensive School).

pupils to take part in sports after leaving school. There were, however, large numbers of pupils for whom this programme was ineffective or inefficient (Figure 2).

Suggested developments

Our experiences in physical education and health education led us to believe that in order for us to achieve our aim of the maximium number of pupils developing a healthy active

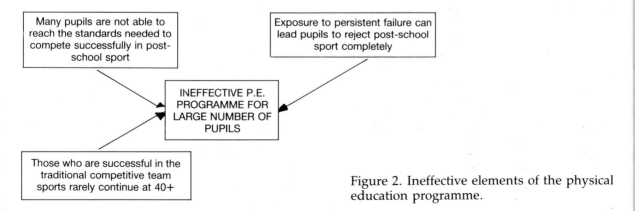

Figure 2. Ineffective elements of the physical education programme.

lifestyle, the physical education programme to be developed would need to do two things:

(i) Rationalize the activities offered so that pupils are given the opportunity to develop skills in, and gain satisfaction from, those types of activity most suited to their individual abilities, physique, personality and personal preference,

and (ii) Develop in the pupils the rational decision-making skills needed for them to be able to devise, develop and modify their own healthy active lifestyle.

(i) Rationalising Activities

In most schools where options are offered, they are offered on the basis of individual activities. Our suggestion is that after a look at a whole range of activities each pupil should be counselled (at 14+) to enable him/her to choose an area of physical education experiences in which he/she would specialise for the final two years of compulsory schooling. This area would be the one most suited to the individual's abilities, personality and personal preference.

Suggested areas of experience
(a) *Aesthetic and body management* activities such as dance and trampolining etc.
(b) *Body Training* activities such as weight training, long distance running etc.
(c) *Outdoor Education* activities such as walking, canoeing, camp craft, map reading, orienteering etc.
(d) *Traditional Competitive team and individual sports* such as soccer, rugby, hockey, netball, basketball etc.
(e) *At Risk* — Those pupils who do not seem to gain pleasure or satisfaction from any of the above areas of experience, yet whose needs with regard to health and fitness are as great as those of anyone else. For these pupils, a programme containing a variety of

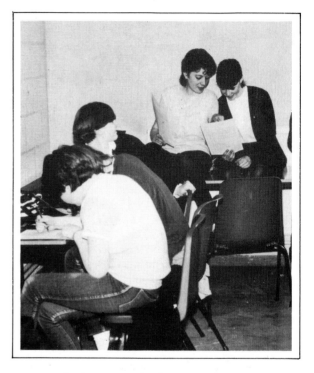

simple fitness and relaxation exercises might be appropriate.

The idea then, is not for pupils to opt for a specific activity, but for a range of activities in an area of physical education experience most suited to their individual needs. Specific activities, such as swimming for example, might easily prove to be an element in any of the areas of choice.

(ii) Decision Making Skills

Alongside the areas of choice, a health and fitness programme needs to be included for all pupils. The content of this programme might be fairly traditional looking at the relationships between exercise, diet, stress and fitness, but the method to be used is drawn particularly from our experiences in health education.

Teaching for Decison-Making in Health Education

Whatever current thinking on health education teaching might be, the traditional teaching method for this and many other subjects is based upon the 'Medical Model'.

This approach to health education teaching has its foundations in the assumption that a direct cause and effect relationship exists between the various elements of the model (Figure 3).

Figure 3.
The Medical Model for Health Education Teaching.

The medical model suggests that provided with information, the pupils will develop knowledge. This knowledge will influence their attitudes and as a result of these changes in attitude they will modify their behaviour. As a result of these changes in behaviour they will become healthier.

Many people have shown this model to be an inaccurate and misleading description of the process of behaviour change. Levin (1973) said "For years health education (in the USA) used the 'tell them the facts' approach. It was found, however, that this had very limited effects on children's health behaviour". Similarly, Guy (1976) suggests, "where information regarding health is in conflict with attitudes, the chances are that the information will be ignored unless young people are given the opportunity to discuss and understand their attitude".

The weight of opinion would seem to suggest that the medical model is much too simplistic and that perhaps a more realistic model for health behaviour is that of Becker and his co-workers (Becker et al., 1977; see Figure 4).

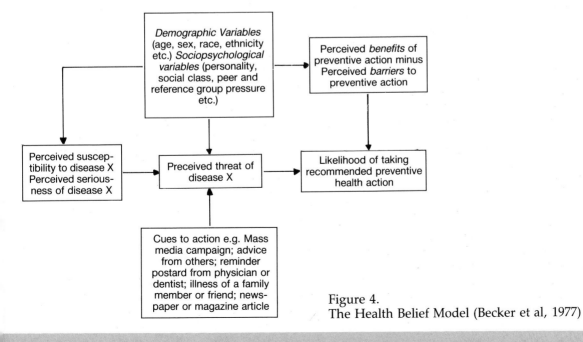

Figure 4.
The Health Belief Model (Becker et al, 1977)

This model would seem to emphasise the importance of attitudes and values in the health decision-making process and if this is the case, then the major weakness in the medical model would seem to be the link between knowledge and attitudes. This theory would support what Guy (1976) suggests and is, in turn, supported by research conducted by Silman (1979) and by Cook (1983) who both found that among the schoolchildren they tested, there existed *strong evidence* of a relationship between *attitudes and behaviour* and *very little evidence* of a relationship between *knowledge and behaviour* with respect to a number of health topics. This suggests that the breakdown would seem to lie between knowledge and attitudes. These attitudes may, of course, be extremely difficult to change especially if, as Guy (1976) suggests, they begin to develop from the moment a child is born, that they develop initially from parents and relations and often reflect the attitudes of the community of which they are part. However, he also suggests that as the social circle of the individual widens, these attitudes are added to, modified or magnified by friends, teachers and others, with peer group pressures being a particularly powerful influence. It is, in fact, this last aspect which Guy suggests can help schools to be successful if they utilise the powerful influence of the peer group. It would seem that many health educationalists would

agree with him, since Wright (1983), reviewing contemporary health education literature, states that,

"Helping pupils to articulate their own ideas, and particularly their attitudes to various health-related issues through guided group discussions, is one of the prime procedures recommended in contemporary health education literature for trying to develop appropriate attitudes and values or to modify the established values of young people so that they are more likely to give rise to health-constructive patterns of behaviour."

After considering much of this evidence, we felt that the three most important factors which should influence the method for teaching health education were:–

(i)   Attitudes and values are much more likely to influence health-related behaviour than knowledge alone.

(ii)   Pupils will find it easier to recognise other peoples attitudes and values than their own.

(iii)   In order to strengthen or modify their own attitudes, pupils would need to compare them with alternative attitudes and values.

Alternative Strategy for teaching Health Education

It was decided to treat each topic as a decision making exercise, and as with any decision-making process, all the information needs to be made available to the pupils at the beginning. This might seem very much like the medical model initially but it is the development which differs. A second point, which should be made is that in a number of the early 'pilot' lessons the individual work was omitted. This did result in a number of the more reserved and perhaps less dominant pupils being unable to make a real contribution. It was found that by starting with the individual work, everyone was able to make a contribution at the later stage of group and class discussion.

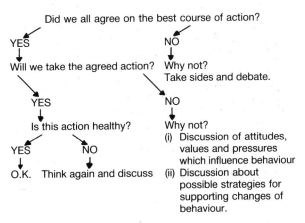

Did we all agree on the best course of action?

YES → Will we take the agreed action? → YES → Is this action healthy? → YES → O.K. NO → Think again and discuss

NO → Why not? Take sides and debate. → NO → Why not?
(i) Discussion of attitudes, values and pressures which influence behaviour
(ii) Discussion about possible strategies for supporting changes of behaviour.

Figure 5. Discussion possibilities.

1. Introduction
The topic is introduced by a talk , a film or some other source material. This introduction might suggest which behaviour is healthy and which is unhealthy.

2. Development I. Individual Work
The students are given a duplicated worksheet which contains:-
(a) Information related to the introduction.
(b) Alternative interpretations and arguments.
(c) Where to find further information.
(d) A series of questions structured to highlight individual attitudes and values, which lead to asking the question, "what should we do in the light of the available evidence?"

3. Development II Group Discussion
The students are then asked to consider individually the problem posed in the worksheet. Having had time to decide on their own responses, the whole group is then divided into small self-selected groups to discuss their responses. One spokesperson is asked to take notes, record the different attitudes and responses, and prepare a summary of what happened during the discussion.

4. Development III Class Discussion
(a) All students return to the class group with the spokesperson relating what happened in each group.
(b) Whole group discussion led by the teacher (see Figure 5).

5. Conclusion — student individual work
The conclusion of the topic has two main aims.

(a) To allow the students the opportunity for reflection to internalise what the topic was about and their responses to it.
(b) To allow the students the opportunity to make constructive criticism of the programme in order to help us to improve it.

In order to achieve these aims, the students are asked to write a report in response to six questions.

(i) What was the topic about?
(ii) What discussions took place?
(iii) What came out of the discussions?
(iv) What made me think most?
(v) Will I change my behaviour in future?
(vi) If yes, why? If no, why not?

It was felt that this method could be adopted or at least adapted to suit a wide range of health topics from something affecting physical health, such as smoking or drinking, to something of a more social and emotional nature such as a role-playing exercise depicting parental attitudes to staying out late.

How can The Health Education Approach be Applied to Physical Education?
I would suggest that there are three main points arising from this discussion of health education teaching methods which could profitably be applied by physical educationists to a health-related fitness course.

(i) Telling the pupils that effective exercise and a balanced diet will help them to lead healthier happier lives is just providing information. It is essential but it is not enough. This is going back to the medical model and it does not work on its own.

(ii) Giving the pupils the necessary knowledge and skills so that they can effectively exercise and diet and therefore devise a healthy active lifestyle is still only providing the tools for the job. It is essential but not enough.

(iii) The key to success might be in enabling the students to examine, develop, modify or reinforce their attitudes and values so that they can develop the rational decision making skills needed to effect any change in lifestyle. This, in my opinion, can only be done through discussion.

What are the practical implications?
The first point to make here is that the purpose of this chapter is not to dismiss alternative attempts at health-related fitness programmes, but if possible to add to them. For this reason, any content which might currently be employed showing the need for fitness along with alternative methods of monitoring and improving it would be extremely valuable. What I believe is needed in addition, however, is the opportunity for pupils to practice decision-making skills, just as one might practice any physical skill, in such a way as to enable the individual to do so safely without fear of making

a mistake. This, I feel, can be done very effectively through role-play.

Suggested method of approach
(i) Pupils cover a basic course in health-related fitness so that they have all the relevant information regarding the need for regular physical activity, balanced diet, reduction of stress etc.

(ii) Having covered the basic course, pupils are given a number of case studies to consider and make recommendations on courses of action. It is suggested that in order to gain maximum participation from pupils, the problems are considered in three phases.
(a) Individually.
(b) In small groups to look at alternative interpretations.
(c) In whole class discussion to gain concensus.

Pupils are given a case study of an individual to consider. It might contain details such as:–

Age
Height
Weight
Present physical condition
Occupation
Family situation
Hobbies
Favourite foods and drinks (including eating and drinking habits)
Methods of transport to work
Stress factors
Spare time available, etc.

Questions to be asked
(a) Should this individual try to do something to improve his/her fitness?

YES   NO

Next question   Why not? Debate later

(b) What are his/her possible options?

regarding Diet
and Exercise — competitive games, jogging, swimming, keep fit classes, multigym weights etc, walk or cycle, to work, outdoor pursuits etc.

(c) What does he/she do at present to maintain or improve fitness?
(d) What problems might he/she face to prevent action being taken?
e.g. lack of skill, tired from work, too busy with work/ housework/looking after children, embarrassed alone, no-one else to work with, expense, weather, time (cycling or walking to work) etc.
(e) What could he/she do successfully to improve fitness?
(f) What is stopping him/her from doing this?
(g) How can the problems be overcome?

By considering a number fo these case studies individuals can, by their own reflection and through discussion with others in the group:–
(i) Develop attitudes which will help them to value physical fitness as an aspect of personal health.
(ii) Appreciate the variety of problems people can face when attempting to devise a healthy active lifestyle.
(iii) Develop the rational decision making skills to enable them to put into practice the lessons they have learned, despite the problems faced.

Conclusions

There have been suggestions that many secondary school physical education programmes would seem to be too traditional and too elitist to meet the needs of the whole range of pupils within the school. Where options have been introduced there has been a tendency merely to provide as many options as possible in the hope that this will educate for leisure.

As a result of such programmes there are large numbers of the adult population who do not have the attitudes, values, knowledge or skills to be able to lead a healthy active life.

I would suggest that for this situation to improve there is a need for balanced physical education programme in which individuals are guided into an area of physical education (in much the same way as they are guided in their choice of academic subjects) which is most suited to their personality, abilities and personal preferences. In particular, those students who are most at risk because of their personality or lack of ability need special attention.

Alongside and integrated into each of these programmes there should be a health and fitness course. Most recent research supports the currently accepted theory that attitudes and values are much more likely to influence health behaviour than health knowledge alone. For this reason there is a need for teachers to strike a balance between teaching for the development of knowledge and teaching for the development of attitudes as influencing factors in the encouragement of healthy behaviour. This concept of teaching for the development of attitudes requires the establishment of a teaching method which involves the pupil experiencing:–
(a) A personal analysis of all the information available.
(b) Small group guided discussion or role-play to expose a variety of attitudes.
(c) Whole class discussion to demonstrate how different attitudes and values can influence decision-making.
(d) Personal reflection and reporting to internalise all the experiences gained from the discussions.

There would seem to be great value in physical educationists applying themselves to the problems of devising such courses, testing them in their schools and discussing their results with others. In this way physical education can develop to meet the changing needs of a changing society.

References
BECKER, M. H. *et al.* (1977) Selected Psychosocial Models and Correlates of Individual Health-Related Behaviours. *Medical Care,* Vol. 15 (5) Supplement.
COOK, S. (1983). *Health Education in a Secondary School: An innovation in action.* Unpublished M.A. dissertation. University of Hull.
GUY, C. J. (1976) Health Education in Schools. *Health Education Journal,* Vol. 35 (3).
HAYDOCK, E. (1979) Catching the fat Girls. *British Journal of Physical Education,* Vol. 10 (5).
KANE, J. E. (1974). *Physical Education in Secondary Schools.* London: Schools Council Research Studies.
LEVIN, L. S. (1973) Lecture to the Society for Health Education, in Department of Education and Science (1977) *Health Education in Schools:* London H.M.S.O.
SILMAN, A. J. (1979) A Survey of Attitudes to Health Among School Leavers. *Health Education Journal,* Vol. 38 (3).
THOMAS, V. (1977) P.E. for Life. *British Journal of Physical Education,* Vol. 8 (4).
WRIGHT, J. (1983). Physical Education and Health Education in M. Mawer (ed.) *Trends in Physical Education: Aspects of Education: 29:* Institute of Education, University of Hull.

This chapter first appeared in the *Bulletin of Physical Education,* 1983, Vol. 19 (2), and is re-printed with permission.

Chapter Fifteen

A Guide to Health-Related Fitness Testing

Stuart Biddle & Ken Fox

An essential element of fitness education is involved with the evaluation of individual student fitness levels. Exercise advice can only be accurate when based on information about each student's fitness needs. Field tests which have been well researched and tested and which are designed for operation in the school setting are now available. Besides being reasonable assessment instruments, these tests have proved to be very useful in helping students understand fitness concepts and, if used with expertise and empathy, can provide motivation for individual fitness improvement. On the other hand, there are examples to show that poor administration of fitness tests can lead to gross inaccuracies, misleading advice, and at worst, alienation of those students with the greatest fitness problems. This chapter is designed to outline some of the more practical and pertinent field tests and at the same time offer guidelines that will help ensure their most effective use.

Those aspects of fitness which are important for health have already been clearly defined in Chapter 1 as:

1. Cardiovascular fitness
2. Muscular fitness, including:
   (a) strength
   (b) muscular endurance
   (c) flexibility
3. Body composition

It is impossible to test overall fitness by using a single test, as each part of health-related fitness is somewhat independent of the others. It is equally difficult to assess all aspects of muscular strength and flexibility using single tests. Each muscle group has its own particular characteristics, and so many tests are necessary for the most accurate picture. For the sake of practicality and simplicity, however, four of the more workable tests have been chosen for description here, which give a reasonable profile of an individual's health-related fitness status.

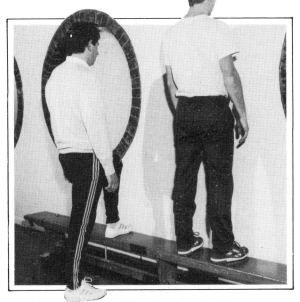

1. An assessment of cardiovascular fitness

The central factor in a person's health and fitness is the condition of the cardiovascular system. The ability of the body to do prolonged muscular work depends upon the ability of the body to deliver oxygen to the working muscles, and this is reflected by the condition of the cardiovascular system. One means of assessing the condition of this system is to run and/or walk as far as possible in twelve minutes.

TEST: Cooper's 12 minute run/walk test.

Equipment: running track
stop watch/clock
corner flags/posts

Procedures:
1. The track should be divided into convenient sections with the corner flags to enable the distance covered by the subject to be fairly accurately recorded in meters, e.g. 400m track divided into ⅛ths.

2. Subjects should be asked to do

their best to cover the maximum possible distance by running and/or walking in 12 minutes.

Scoring: Record the distance covered to the nearest 25m.

Additional notes:

1. Students (particularly females) who are relatively untrained often lack localised muscular endurance in their legs. When they attempt to run or walk fast, these muscles fatigue rapidly and do not allow the cardiovascular system to be adequately stressed for an accurate assessment of its capacity. It is recommended that 3 to 4 weeks of moderate exercise using leg muscles be completed for relatively inactive students before a 12-minute run is attempted. For this and other reasons, fitness testing during the first couple of weeks of term is usually not a good idea.

2. Some experience of pacing is needed to appreciate the task involved. At least one practice run is recommended of 12 minutes duration, which is preceeded by pacing advice.

3. An efficient means of administering the test is to pair off the subjects and have one person count the distance covered. Nearing the end of the run the counter should go to the anticipated finishing location of their partner.

4. The accuracy of the 12-minute run is dependent on environmental conditions. Efforts should be made to avoid testing in adverse conditions such as wind and rain, and to duplicate conditions from one testing session to another if results are to be compared longitudinally. Also, for obvious reasons, consideration should be given to factors such as exercising immediately after lunch.

5. Other field tests of cardiovascular fitness have also been validated. The AAHPERD Health-related Fitness Test recommends using the 1.5 mile walk/run, and also the variety of step tests available can be considered field tests suitable for the gymnasium or home setting.

6. This test requires all-out effort in order to be a true test of aerobic power, hence motivation is a key issue. Teachers should not expect valid results unless the reasons for the test and its personal relevance have been emphasised to students before the test is administered.

7. Useful teacher references:
   (i) Corbin, C.B. & Lindsey, R. (1983) *Fitness for Life.* Glenview, Il.: Scott Foresman, Ch.4.
   (ii) Corbin, C.B. & Lindsey, R. (1985) *Concepts of physical Fitness.* Dubuque, Iowa: Wm.C. Brown, Chs. 2 & 12 (5th Ed).

Norms

Norms tables are available for the 12 minute run test (see AAHPERD, 1985). However, caution must be expressed here since comparison with others does not necessarily indicate what is 'healthy' or otherwise. An individual's score is a result of genetic ability as well as physical conditioning. The reader is referred to the 'General Guidelines' section at the end of this chapter, and to chapter 16.

Exercise Prescription

Employ the "F.I.T.T." principle (Corbin & Lindsey, 1985).

F	frequency	How often?
I	intensity	How much?
T	time	How long?
T	type	What exercises?

For cardiovascular (aerobic) fitness

Frequency: minimum of 3 times per week.

Intensity: enough to elevate the heart rate usually to between 60-80% of maximum.

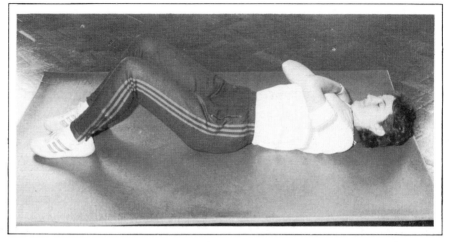

Figure 1.

Maximum = 220-age (approximate guidelines only).

Time: Minimum 15 minutes per session.

Type: Rhythmic exercises such as jogging, cycling, swimming, continuous games.

2. An assessment of muscular strength/ endurance

The maintenance of good muscular condition and body posture is important for health. As previously mentioned, it would take many individual tests which are specific to each muscle group to achieve an accurate overall picture of an individual's muscular condition. The muscles of the trunk region, notably the abdominals, need to be kept in first class condition to help protect against one of the major health complaints; low back pain. The abdominals provide support for the natural curvature of the spine and if they are kept in good condition, enhance posture and protect against injury. A well-established test for this region is the sit-up test.

TEST: Sit-ups in 1 minute.

Equipment: Gymnastic mats.

Procedures: Give a clear demonstration of the sit-up technique emphasising:

    (i) arms crossed on chest, hands on front shoulders;

    (ii) start position is lying flat on the back with knees bent and soles of feet flat on the floor about 12-18″ from buttocks.

    (iii) partner sits on subject's feet and holds the legs firmly by passing arms between thigh and calves;

    (iv) sit-up is executed from the supine position, curl-up until the elbows touch the thighs (not twisting), then return until the shoulder blades touch the mat.

    (v) For the abdominals to be fully activated, it is important to shorten the distance between the rib cage and lower pelvic girdle. To achieve this, the head should be curled forward with the chin on the chest as the movement proceeds (see Figure 1).

Scoring: Complete number of sit-ups in 1 minute.

Additional notes:

1. There is considerable scope for not operating this exercise through the full range of movement so that inflated scores result. Instructors need to constantly emphasise good technique and to allow students to practice. If the importance of personal

Intensity: a resistance (weight or bodyweight) allowing for 8-10 repetitions in good style but with effort required (Variations on this will allow the emphasis to be swtiched between endurance and strength).

Time: each session 30 minutes; i.e. approximately 3 sets of 8+ repetitions on 6-8 exercises (less repetitions for strength).

Type: body weight resistance exercises; external weight resistance exercises.

Notes
(i) Students should avoid timed circuits if the speed element causes poor exercise technique.
(ii) it is possible to perform some localised muscular endurance exercises, such as sit-ups and press-ups, on consecutive days.

improvement dominates over a need to beat others, and the futility of false results outlined, students will endeavour to achieve accurate and valid scores on these tests.
2. For most students, the number of repetitions they will perform on this exercise will mean that they are assessing muscular endurance rather than strength. Maximal strength testing can be a problematic area for young or unfit people due to the stresses involved, although simple hand-grip tests, for example, are possible. See Corbin & Lindsey (1983, 1985) for further ideas on illustrating strength through field tests or other 'stunts'.
3. Useful teacher references:
   (i) Corbin, C.B. & Lindsey, R. (1983). *Fitness for Life*. Glenview, Il.: Scott Foresman, Chs. 5 & 6.
   (ii) Corbin, C.B. & Lindsey, R. (1985). *Concepts of physicaıl fitness*. Dubuque, Iowa: Wm.C. Brown, Chs. 7, 8 & 13 (5th Ed).

Exercise Prescription (for development of muscle strength/endurance)
Frequency: about 3 times per week.

3. An assessment of flexibility

Flexibility has been defined as 'the range of motion of a joint or joint complex'. One of the major elements of joint mobility is the length of muscles involved in moving the joint, with lack of length limiting movement. Once again, flexibility is joint specific and different tests are needed to measure each one. Of particular significance to health are the muscles involved with the lower back and back of the legs (hamstrings) because their lack of length is related to low-back pain. This can be estimated by the sit-and-reach test.

TEST: Sit and reach test of flexibility

Equipment: Gymnastic benches. Ruler.

Procedures: 1. Ensure that all students are throughly warmed-up particularly in the hamstring and lower back region.

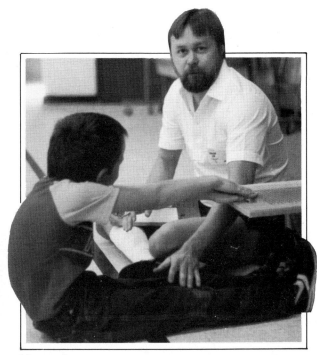

Figure 2.

5. A static stretch position must be held before reading off the score. No jerking or bouncing movements are to be allowed. (See Figure 2.)

Scoring: Note that the ruler extends 15cms. over the bench, hence the subject who can only just reach his/her toes scores 15cms.

Additional notes:
1. Encourage a gradual reaching forward into the stretch position by emphasising a stretch from the hips – not from the shoulders.
2. Useful teacher references:
   (i) Anderson, R. (1980). *Stretching.* London: Pelham. Whilst this book contains a variety of stretching exercises, it also shows some contraindicated ones. Nevertheless, it is a comprehensive pictorial source of stretching routines.
   (ii) Corbin, C.B. & Lindsey, R. (1983). *Fitness for Life.* Glenview, Il.: Scott Foresman, Ch. 7.
   (iii) Corbin, C.B. & Lindsey, R. (1985). *Concepts of physical fitness.* Dubuque, Iowa: Wm.C. Brown, Chs. 9 & 14 (5th Ed).

Exercise Prescription (for development of flexibility).
Frequency: minimum 3 times per week; can be done daily.

Intensity: stretch in slow and controlled manner until a feeling of MILD TENSION is felt. Do NOT bounce into stretched positions.

Time: Hold stretch for 5-30 seconds; repeat 3 times each exercise.

Type: Numerous static stretching exercises are available (see teacher references). For maximum gains in

2. Prior to testing:
   (a) turn gym benches onto their sides.
   (b) tape a ruler onto the top of the upturned bench so that it overlaps 15cms with the zero end nearest the subject. The ruler projects at right angles to the face of the bench, extending towards the student.
   (c) ensure all benches are secured to prevent slipping.

3. Student sits on the floor with legs together; feet should be placed flat against the upturned bench with shoes off.

4. By keeping the legs straight and back of the knees of the ground (with partner assistance if necessary), the student slowly reaches forward as far as possible along the ruler, ensuring at all times that both hands are streched out equally, one on top of the other.

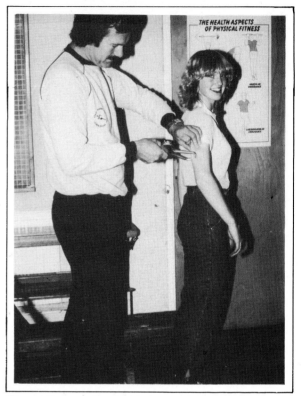

Figure 3.

flexibility, muscles must be warm. Stretching at the end of a work-out is therefore favoured for flexibility improvement. Stretching should also be used as part of a warm-up and general preparation for exercise!

4. An assessment of body fatness

The measurement of body fatness as a component of health-related fitness can be justified on the basis that excessive, as well as inadequate amounts, of body fat can be a health problem. Whilst relatively few British P.E. teachers are skilled in skinfold measurement, it is an area which can be developed and practiced. Clearly, the P.E teacher has an important role to play in fat control, particularly through teaching appropriate exercise.

A reasonably simple way to assess body fat is by measuring a skinfold pinch at the site of the triceps. This is quite a good correlate with total body fatness although a combination of body sites (e.g. subscapular, iliac crest) is advantageous if time is available. Readers are referred to the teacher references in this section for more detail on body composition measures.

TEST: Triceps skinfold measurement.

Equipment: skinfold calipers (available from: P.E.A.)

Procedures:
1. Have subject stand erect with right arm hanging losely at the side of the body.
2. The tester locates the right triceps (back of upper arm) and pinches the skinfold as follows:
   (i) mid-way between shoulder and elbow
   (ii) pinch across the vertical skinfold, as shown in Figure 3, with thumb and forefinger.
3. Ensure that the skinfold is pulled away from the muscle.
4. Close the calipers slowly around the skinfold until the calipers have full tension. Read off the scale after 2 seconds (allowing the dial to settle with body fluids being released from the site).
5. Ensure that the calipers are placed on the skinfold mid-way between the skinfold crest and the base, and approximately one inch from the fingers.

Scoring: Record the caliper reading and repeat the measurement THREE times. To reduce errors, record the *middle* score (i.e. scores of 14, 15, 13 would lead to 14 being recorded).

Additional notes:
1. Teachers are advised to practice these procedures to improve reliability and validity and, if possible, compare scores with a more experienced skinfolder. The most common source of error results from incorrect location

of the skinfold sites.

2. Some students are very sensitive about their body image and in particular their levels of body fatness. Many obese children already suffer embarrassment in the physical education setting and do their utmost to avoid it. Every effort must be taken to preserve the dignity of these students and it is recommended that skinfolding be carried out away from the rest of the class, at least until an atmosphere of empathy and understanding has been created.

3. Although excess body fatness is a threat to health, a further problem has recently emerged among adolescent girls; that of too little body fat, and a tendency towards anorexia nervosa. Teachers should be sensitive to this problem and refer suspected cases for medical intervention. While encouraging a concern for the health problems associated with overfatness, the teacher has to tread a fine line by discouraging obsession with losing body fat.

4. Useful teacher references:
   (i) Corbin, C.B. & Lindsey, R. (1983). *Fitness for Life*. Glenview, Il.: Scott Foresman, Ch.8.
   (ii) Corbin, C.B. & Lindsey, R. (1985). *Concepts of physical fitness*. Dubuque, Iowa: Wm.C. Brown, Ch. 10.

Norms

Caution must be expressed in the use of body fat norms tables. When compared with a population which is greatly overfat, it would hardly be desirable to be normal or 'average'. In addition, there are no advantages, and possible dangers, especially for females, involved with extremely low body fat levels. In many cases 'less' is not necessarily 'better'. There is clearly a wide range of body fatness which can be considered perfectly healthy, and different body types may be more comfortable at different levels within that range (see chapter 7). Of more significance is the rate and direction of change in an individual's body fat levels, so that continuous monitoring should receive most attention.

Exercise Prescription (for bodyfat reduction)

Frequency: daily exercise and general increases in physical activity.

Intensity: fat loss is best achieved with extended low-moderate intensity exercise.

Time: Each session, therefore, should last a minimum of 15 minutes although longer sessions are more effective.

Type: steady aerobic exercises seem best but a general daily increase in activity levels will be beneficial. Clearly exercise is only half of the 'problem'. Effective fat control is achieved through appropriate regulation of exercise and eating/ drinking habits.

Some General Guidelines for Fitness Testing

The key to effective fitness testing lies in the level of understanding of the teacher/instructor. If the reasons behind fitness testing are soundly based on educational principles, and the limitations of fitness testing thoroughly understood then there is little to prevent them being useful tools in fitness education. Problems of validity and reliability can be greatly reduced if the emphasis is placed on the individual and his/her understanding of their personal fitness.

The objective of health-related fitness programmes is to encourage the lifetime fitness of students and it is essential to work out how fitness testing can best achieve this. Typically it has been assumed that fitness testing will help motivate students become fitter. This can be the case, but unfortunately there are equally many ways in which fitness tests might cause students to 'turn off' to fitness activity.

In addition, all fitness tests are subject to gross error, some of which are depicted in Figure 4. Field tests are particularly prone because control has been forfeited for the sake of convenience. As educators, we are basically concerned with the element of a fitness test score which is due to the state of training or conditioning of the student. Unfortunately, this can be masked by other factors such as genetic differences, stage of maturation, tester error, and changes in testing conditions.

The above factors have important implications to fitness testing procedures and their recognition should cause the tester to PROCEED WITH CAUTION.

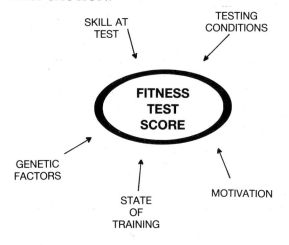

Figure 4. Factors affecting fitness test score.

A large component of any fitness score, but especially cardiovascular fitness scores, is provided by the genetic component. Teachers have to have an in-built awareness that many students have distinct starting advantages when it comes to performance on a fitness test (see Figure 5). This may be due to superior heart and circulation physiology in the case of the elite long distance runner or swimmer, or fast-twitch muscle fibre-typing in the case of the

GENETIC FACTORS

- Muscle fibre type
- Heart and circulation morphology
- Stage of maturation
- Body size and somatotype
- Sensitivity to training

Figure 5.
Genetic factors affecting fitness test score.

faster and more powerful sprinters. Other advantages may simply lie in body type or stage of maturation. Yet, as health-related fitness educators, we are concerned with that part of fitness that can be changed through regular physical activity, because health is more important than athletic performance, and so genetic variance and maturational stage can be regarded as potential problems.

This genetic handicapping makes the comparison of one individual to another very tentative. Norms tables can be useful in giving teachers and students an idea of where they stand, and providing a baseline from which to work, but constant comparisons between students on the basis of raw fitness test scores goes a long way towards undermining the usefulness of testing. Similarly, reward or grading systems based on fitness test performances merely encourages those already blessed with ability (usually these are competent sports players as well), and provides yet another discouraging piece of news for those not genetically endowed. These are often the less powerful, fatter, and poorly co-ordinated individuals who already avoid physical activity because of their lack of success in sports settings. They are the students in most need of health-related fitness help and so we must do our utmost not to discourage them from what may be considered a new beginning in physical activity.

Clearly, in order to encourage all students, success must be based on effort and improvement in fitness, at least to a minimum level for health, bearing in mind that not everyone can achieve the 'excellent' category, regardless of how hard they try. Students should clearly understand this message. Fitness test information should therefore be collected longitudinally and be based around an individual's improvement for the most effective results.

If we are to expect students to make the decision to be active, we must explain clearly the benefits of health-related fitness. Similarly, if we ask students to exert maximum effort on a test of fitness, they should be fully aware of the reasons for doing it.

The teacher who forces his/her students to take part in a 12-minute run during the first week of term without previous discussion on aspects of cardiovascular fitness, should expect invalid results due to lack of motivation. For this reason it is recommended that block administration of fitness test 'batteries' be avoided where possible. Fitness tests are best incorporated into comprehensive courses of study on health-related fitness and administered when they become relevant to the subject matter.

It also makes little sense to expose students to their fitness problems without providing an adequate back-up service to help solve problems. This has the same effect as labelling a student as 'stupid' in a maths class without offering to give tuition. If fitness testing is a component of the P.E. programme, then exercise advice should be available, fitness problem-solving skills should be taught, and opportunities provided for a wide range of fitness activities both within and outside the curriculum.

An ultimate goal of fitness education is to make students 'fitness independent'. They should be capable of constantly monitoring their fitness levels and regulating their physical activity to bring about the right fitness changes. Fitness testing should eventually, therefore, cease to be something we 'do to' students and be placed in the hands of students themselves. Such self-evaluation is a skill that requires considerable practice and so should receive increasing emphasis as the programme progresses.

In conclusion, it should be recognised that self-evaluation exercises (fitness tests) can be valuable learning tools if the cautionary remarks mentioned are understood. They should not feature as *the* central issue of health-related fitness yet can provide information for illustrating fitness concepts and for the development of fitness skills. They may also provide a useful focus for initiating work in other areas of the curriculum, such as science, mathematics and home economics.

References
In addition to the teacher references already listed, readers are referred to:
American Alliance of Health, Physical Education, Recreation and Dance (1985). *Health-related physical fitness test manual.* AAPHERD, 1900, Association Drive, Reston, VA22091, U.S.A.

Chapter Sixteen

A Critique of Fitness Testing

Neil Armstrong

The current emphasis on health-related fitness courses in schools seems to have re-generated interest in field or performance tests of physical fitness. These tests may be justified from a pedagogical or psychological viewpoint. They may be valuable teaching aids in stimulating interest, intoducing new concepts in health-related fitness or in helping children to understand their bodies. They are *not*, however, generally based on sound physiological foundations and are of little value in the complex analysis and assessment of children's fitness. Many of the data are meaningless, not capable of rigorous interpretation, and more likely to cause confusion than solve problems.

All performance tests are primarily dependent upon motivation and this was vividly illustrated by Schwab (1953) who required subjects to hang on a horizontal bar in a manner similar to the test recommended to assess the local muscular endurance of girls in the Handbook for the Assessment of Physical Fitness (PEA, 1978). Schwab found that with instructions to hold on "as long as possible" the average length of time before letting go was less than 1 minute. With a 5 dollar reward promised for beating their previous record subjects managed to hang on for an average of nearly 2 minutes. So their "local muscular endurance" was doubled with a financial inducement!

Several writers emphasise the use of norm tables in providing feedback to subjects, but how can tables constructed on the basis of chronological age provide worthwhile information about children at different levels of skeletal and biological maturation? With a class of third year boys at the end of January a teacher may be testing a group in which 20% are pre-pubertal, 20% are at puberty stage 5 and the remainder somewhere in between. The effects of growth and maturation on performance and children's responses to exercise and training are well documented and interested readers are directed to more detailed

analyses (Armstrong and Davies, 1984; Boileau, 1984). However, let me briefly examine some tests in order to illustrate the physiological limitations of health-related fitness testing.

No one parameter can fully describe cardio-respiratory fitness but it is widely recognised that the best single physiological indicator is maximal oxygen uptake (VO_2 max). Therefore the results of any test claiming to measure cardiorespiratory fitness must be strongly correlated with VO_2 max if the test is to be judged valid. The coefficients of correlation between children's 12 minute run/walk distances and VO_2 max have been shown to be very variable and usually disappointingly low. La Riviére et al (1974), for example, found a correlation coefficient of 0.44 between the 12 minute run/walk distances and VO_2 max of boys i.e. a common variance of less than 20%! In fact in normal children the prediction of VO_2 max from an endurance run is little better than can be obtained from parameters of body size and composition and Shepard (1982) suggests performance tests may merely be a complicated method of identifying tall or fat pupils. The lack of relationship between run/walk scores and VO_2 max is not really surprising when one considers how strongly influenced running tests are by environment, pace judgement, running efficiency and body composition as well as the motivation of the child to do well.

VO_2 max increases gradually during childhood and then during puberty there is a dramatic increase in boys' VO_2 max which corresponds to the time of peak height velocity and increased secretion of male hormones (androgens). These changes result in hypertrophy of skeletal and cardiac muscle, stimulation of red cell and haemoglobin production, and the proliferation of metabolic enzymes which together make possible large increases in cardiorespiratory fitness. Pre-pubertal children have a limited ability for cardiac hypertrophy and metabolic enzyme synthesis and do not seem to respond to endurance training as well as more mature children and adults.

Muscular strength and endurance are specific to each muscle group and there is no single test which is able to accurately define an individual's muscular fitness. Muscular endurance tests such as sit ups, often wrongly used as tests of strength, are notorious for their reliance upon motivation.

Sexually immature children have low levels of androgens and maximal strength-gaining potential is not possible until adult levels of androgens are achieved. The extent of the development and performance of muscle is also dependent on the relative maturation of the nervous system which is not complete until sexual maturity has been reached. The immature child cannot, therefore, be expected to respond to strength training or achieve the same performances as the mature child. When this information is combined with the fact that immature children also have a lower concentratrion of the glycolytic rate limiting enzyme phosphofructokinase, the value of sit-up norms is put into perspective.

Flexibility is joint specific and there is no single indicator of body flexibility. It is a popular belief that young children are very flexible and then gradually lose this flexibility as they grow older. The scientific evidence for this premise is extremely limited and "flexibility" seems to vary with the test administered. Leighton (1956) reported a steady downward trend with age (10 to 18 year old boys) in the range of motion of a majority of the joint movements he measured with his flexometer. On the other hand, Renson et al (1971) studying 12 to 19 year old boys found a progressive increase in flexibility with age as indicated by the sit and reach test, but this was not confirmed with either a trunk twist of ankle flexibility test. Huprich and Sigerseth (1950) reported no significant differences among girls aged 9 to 15 years on six different flexibility test items.

I am unaware of any investigations showing on a scientific basis how training of flexibility affects children. However, during growth the legs become proportionally longer in relation to the trunk and this change in the ratio trunk length/leg length will undoubtedly influence sit and reach scores to such an extent that the use of norms with children must be questionable.

Children's body fat content is typically estimated from an adult model which wrongly assumes that the child's body composition is chemically mature. A significant change in the relationship between anthropometric dimensions and body fatness as estimated from body density takes place between 8 and 15 years of age. The interpretation of children's skinfold data (e.g. triceps skinfold) in terms of total body fatness cannot therefore be made at the present time.

During childhood girls have slightly more fat than boys but at puberty there are marked

changes in body composition. Boys significantly increase their lean mass and decrease their fat percentage, typically by three to five percent between 12 and 17 years. Girls increase both their lean mass and body fat. Physical activity will not change the essence of these growth related stages of body composition. Vigorous training during adolescence will not prevent the increase in girls' body fat although the gains may well be less than in sedentary girls. The value of body fat norm tables (derived from skinfold data) in a population of children at different stages of development is extremely limited.

Performance or field tests simply determine the obvious and distinguish the mature child from the immature child. They may be of value as a pedagogical tool (as argued in chapter 15) but they are of limited use in the assessment of children's fitness. Before teachers waste many hours "teaching time" attempting to assess fitness, but really assessing the potency of the motivational conditions under which they were collecting data of questionable value, perhaps we should re-evaluate the role of health-related fitness testing in schools.

References
ARMSTRONG, N. and DAVIES, B. (1984). The metabolic and physiological responses of children to exercise and training, *Physical Education Review*.
BOILEAU, R.A. (1984). *Advances in Pediatric Sport Sciences*, Champaign, Illinois, Human Kinetics.
HUPRICH, F.L. and SIGERSETH, P.O. (1950). Specificity of flexibility in girls. *Research Quarterly*.
LA RIVIÉRE, G., LAVELLÉE, M. and SHEPHARD, R.J. (1974). Correlations between field tests of performance and laboratory measures of fitness, *Acta Paediatrica Belgica*.
LEIGHTON, J.R. (1956). Flexibility characteristics of males ten to eighteen years of age. *Archives of Physical Medicine and Rehabilitation*.
Physical Education Association (1978). *Handbook for the Assessment of Physical Fitness*, London, PEA.
RENSON, R., BRENNEN, G. and VAN GERVEN, D. (1972). Relation entre des measures somatiques et les résultats de certain tests de sopuplesse. *Kinanthropologie*.
SCHWARD, R.S. (1953). Motivation in measurements of fatigue, in *Symposium On Fatigue (ed. W.F. Floyd and A.T. Welford)*, London, Lewis.
SHEPHARD, R.J. (1982). *Physical Activity and Growth*, London, Year Book Publishers, 1982.

Chapter Seventeen

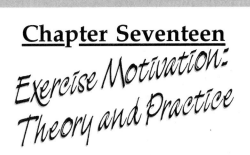

Stuart Biddle

The apparent physiological benefits of regular and appropriate exercise have been well documented (see chapter 3). Many people involved in the promotion of health-related fitness have at least minimal levels of knowledge about the physiological responses of the body to exercise. Unfortunately, the contribution made by psychology to the study of physical activity has predominantly been in the area of sport. Most books on the subject cover a wide variety of competition-related issues from anxiety to zen, yet rarely does one read about the psychology of the exercise participant. The purpose of this chapter, therefore, is to focus on exercise psychology, making specific reference to the problem of staying with an exercise programme. The chapter will deal with three main areas:

a) evidence for exercise participants 'dropping out';
b) factors influencing adherence for starting and maintaining an exercise programme;
c) practical guidelines for starting and maintaining an exercise programme.

Space does not allow for expansion on many of the issues raised. Readers are referred to Dishman (1981a, 1982, 1984) for more detail on the adherence problem.

Quitting exercise

Many people start exercising yet are unable to continue on a regular or permanent basis. I call this the 'New Year Resolution Syndrome'. Research in medical settings has often reported similar findings with compliance rates for medication, attendance at clinics etc. being low. About one third of patients fail to follow physicians' advice, and in some groups non-compliance can be greater than 60% (Becker, 1979). Dishman (1984) suggests that over half those who begin a programme of health-related fitness quit within the first six months, with the greatest dropout occuring early in the programme. Figure 1 shows a typical dropout

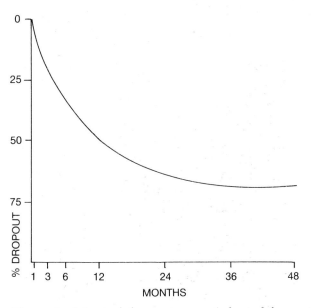

Figure 1. A typical dropout curve (adapted from Carmody et al., 1980; Oldridge, 1982).

curve.

In a study of dropouts from the seven year Ontario Exercise Heart Collaborative Study of post-coronary men (Andrew et al., 1981), it was found that high dropout was related to the convenience of the exercise location, perceptions of the exercise programme (unenthusiastic about exercise, perceived greater exercise fatigue, weak beliefs in the value of exercise), and family/lifestyle factors (high dropout associated with physically demanding jobs and lack of spouse support). Interestingly, a small study of dropouts from an endurance exercise programme reported that dropouts had significantly fewer 'slow-twitch' muscle fibres than those who continued with the programme. It could be that constitutional factors affecting the suitability of certain exercise regimens may contribute to the adherence problem (Ingjer & Dahl, 1979). Similarly, research by Dishman and his co-workers has consistently found that those

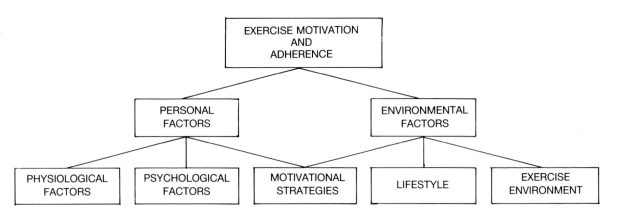

Figure 2. A summary of factors influencing exercise adherence (adapted and modified from Dishman, 1984).

high in percentage bodyfat are more prone to drop out (Dishman, 1981b, 1981c; Dishman & Gettman, 1980).

Factors influencing adherence

It should be evident that the problem of motivation for exercise is a multidimensional one. Figure 2 summarises the main factors influencing adherence.

Personal factors

Somewhat surprisingly, many of the psychological factors one would have thought would predict adherence, such as attitudes and certain personality traits, have not shown consistent results. It is only when extreme groups are compared do differences become evident. This could partly be due to a lack of sophistication in study designs and/or failure to use more specific measuring instruments. For example, the weak results obtained from locus of control studies may be attributable to the unsuitability of the measuring scales. Developments in the assessment of physical fitness locus of control (Whitehead, 1985) may shed some light on this issue. Some health belief factors, whilst not predicting adherence per se, have been shown to link with exercise adoption (Lindsay-Reid & Osborn, 1980), jogging versus non-exercising behaviour (Slenker et al., 1984) and exercise frequency (Biddle & Ashford, 1985). Future work should also account for recent models of estimation and attraction to physical activity (Fox, Corbin & Couldry, 1985; Sonstroem, 1978).

The one psychological trait that seems to have consistently predicted adherence is the general factor of 'self-motivation' (Dishman, 1981c; Dishman & Ickes, 1981; Dishman, Ickes & Morgan, 1980). Dishman (1982) defines this construct as "a generalised non-specific tendency to persist in habitual behaviour regardless of extrinsic reinforcement and is thus largely independent of situational influence". Psychometric advances have been made and the use of the 'Self-Motivation Inventory' (SMI; Dishman & Ickes, 1981), should assist in better predictions of adherers and dropouts.

As suggested earlier, there are important physiological factors influencing exercise behaviour. Dishman & Gettman (1980), in a study of exercise adherers and dropouts, found that the most discriminating variables between the two groups were percent body fat, self motivation and body weight. When subjects were classified as adherers or dropouts on the basis of their scores on these three variables alone, 80% were correctly placed. Dishman & Gettman (1980) concluded that the exercise adherer is characterised by being leaner, lighter and more self-motivated. Many explanations are tenable as to why this is the case. Lighter and leaner individuals many find exercise less demanding, for example, or they may lead more active lifestyles. Alternatively, the fatter, heavier people may be receiving less reinforcement for their efforts, at least as far as appearance is concerned. Research also suggests other biological differences between adherers and dropouts (Dishman, 1982).

Environmental factors

Psychological research has consistently found that individual characteristics alone will only

Figure 2 shows that motivational strategies relate to both personal and environmental factors. These are strategies that can change behaviour and hence alter the chances of staying with an exercise programme.

Practical guidelines

Practical motivating strategies should account for both personal and environmental factors. Similarly, it should be noted whether the individual is starting or attempting to continue involvement, although many of the stategies are equally applicable to both. The following sections, therefore, are brief summaries of a selection of strategies.

account for some of the variance in behaviour. Environmental factors will also affect the adherence process. For example, the study by Andrew et al. (1981) cited earlier found that the convenience of the exercise setting was an important factor. Group factors can also affect motivation (Brawley, 1979). Most people find it easier to exercise with others, and it is only those high in self-motivation who are likely to persist in solo exercise routines. Large exercise groups, however, will not suit everyone and it may be best to seek out smaller groups initially.

The lifestyle of the exerciser can influence the decision to stay with a programme. For example, research has shown that inactive leisure habits relate to greater dropout proneness. Similarly, support from spouses or significant others can be influential. In summary, environmental factors are important and many can be modified to enhance motivation. However, as Dishman (1984) states, "it is ironic that many of the lifestyle components that seem to be related to an increased likelihood of quitting exercise, are also believed to be factors that exaggerate the risk of developing coronary heart disease. Thus from the standpoint of health, people who may need to exercise the most appear most likely to quit!" (Dishman, 1984, p.424).

(A) STRATEGIES FOR STARTING EXERCISE: PERSONAL

A1.   find an exercise partner; you are much more likely to continue at times when you feel less than enthusiastic if someone else is there to encourage you.

A2.   analyse your motives for wanting to start exercising. For example, health, body shape, social contact, challenge, etc. will all determine the type of exercise chosen and the satisfaction gained.

A3.   construct a timetable which clearly indicates the times/days when you and your partner will exercise. These are 'exercise times' and should not be lost to other commitments. If you say to yourself "I'll fit in the exercise when I can", you are doomed to failure. Make a definite time commitment (see Figure 3).

A4.   Psychologists have known for some time that what you say to yourself can have considerable impact on your behaviour. We need to operate what Mahoney & Mahoney (1976) call "cognitive ecology (how to clean up your personal environment)". In other words, make sure that what we say to ourselves is positive and helpful. Negative self-statements such as "I'm not made to exercise" or "I'm naturally fat so there's little point in trying to

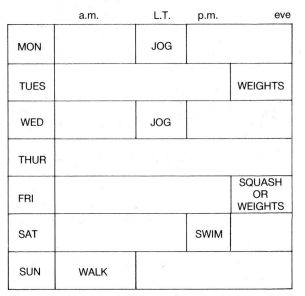

	a.m.	L.T.	p.m.	eve
MON		JOG		
TUES				WEIGHTS
WED		JOG		
THUR				
FRI				SQUASH OR WEIGHTS
SAT			SWIM	
SUN	WALK			

Figure 3. An example exercise timetable: a useful motivational strategy.

lose weight" will prove disastrous. Be realistic but positive.

A5.   start with regular but LOW INTENSITY exercise. You will need to make gradual and comfortable changes to your lifestyle to accommodate exercise. Radical changes or over-enthusiastic exercising will only serve to put people off. The competitive 'no pain – no gain' philosophy is inappropriate for lifetime fitness activities. We must therefore set realistic goals which we can accommodate relatively easily in the first instance, hence the exercise needs to be low intensity and enjoyable.

(B) STRATEGIES FOR STARTING EXERCISE: ENVIRONMENTAL

B1.   chose a form of exercise which you and your partner are likely to find: a) accessible and convenient; b) suitable for your motives (see A2).

B2.   if joining an exercise group, check that the size of the group and the type of exercise are suitable for you.

(C) STRATEGIES FOR MAINTAINING EXERCISE: PERSONAL

C.1   it is only to be expected that occasionally we lose momentum or enthusiasm for exercise. At this stage one should:

a) identify the problem(s) (e.g. 'not enough time')

b) identify alternative strategies (e.g. arrange a lift to work and run home, or reappraise your exercise timetable)

c) put into action the alternative which seems most likely to work. Leave the other alternatives until later.

C2.   use exercise goals. However, these should not necessarily be 'performance' based in the sports sense. It may be better to focus on your exercise BEHAVIOUR rather than your exercise performance. For example, set goals for increasing the regularity of exercising or the duration of an exercise session. Goals should be:

a) specific and measurable

b) realistic but challenging

c) not too distant in time (long term goals are acceptable but use short term goals along the way)

Remember that your goals should be such that changes in your lifestyle are gradual and comfortable.

C3.   use extrinsic rewards sparingly. Try and 'reward' yourself through 'self-reinforcement' and personal self-statements (Biddle, 1984; 1986). When occasional rewards are given, ensure that you are exercising because you want to rather than solely to obtain the reward. A useful strategy is to operate the 'Premack Principle'. This is where you reinforce a 'difficult' behaviour (e.g. exercise) with an 'easy' behaviour (e.g. relaxing watching television). In other words, the television will act as an incentive to complete the exercise routine (see Gillie & Raby, 1984). Various behaviour modification techniques have been successful in changing exercise behaviours (Buffone et al., 1984; Epstein et al., 1980; Kau & Fischer, 1974).

An important point to note on reinforcement is that it is unlikely that exercisers will 'see' the

fruits of their efforts for sometime. For example, a weight control programme takes time to produce fat loss. For this reason, other types of behaviours, such as frequency of attending the exercise class, need to be rewarded. Many people drop out before physiological effects are evident, hence regular monitoring of these effects in the early stages is not recommended.

C4.   as with the strategies for starting exercise (A4), the use of positive personal statements can greatly enhance the maintenance process. For example, it is important that any successes we experience are attributed to our own efforts and that difficulties encountered should be attributed to controllable and changeable factors. Biddle & Ashford (1985) found that one of the strongest predictors of health motivation was the perception of personal control over ones' own health (controllability attribution). Negative personal statements need to be changed so that people can see a way forward through their own efforts.

(D) STRATEGIES FOR MAINTAINING EXERCISE: ENVIRONMENTAL

D1.   analyse your lifestyle and ask yourself "how active is it?" Try and become more active generally and in this way you are more likely to see exercise as being congruent with your overall lifestyle. Use the stairs instead of the lift; walk instead of driving, if possible.

D2.   make your environment work in your favour. This is what Buffone et al. (1984) call 'stimulus control' whereby the environmental cues that encourage exercise are increased. Examples are as follows:

   a) make your exercise timetable highly visible;

   b) write out a personally motivating statement which will encourage you to exercise. Again, make this highly visible, especially in places you are likely to be at times when you can exercise;

   c) if you want to exercise when you return home at the end of the day (but are often less enthusiastic by then), have your exercise clothes laid out ready before you leave in the morning;

   d) if dietary control is a problem alongside your exercise, make food less visible and available.

Just as we try to develop a positive 'personal environment' through self-statements, so we must engineer a conducive 'physical environment' (Mahoney & Mahoney, 1976).

D3.   try and get friends/relatives on your side. Spouse support is a major contributor to exercise motivation. Initially, you should accommodate exercise such that it is not too disruptive to social relationships. Later on one might attempt to integrate these people into your exercise programme. Similarly, 'modelling' can clearly affect behaviour, through the processes of imitation and observation. Thus, teachers of exercise should be appropriate role models by being good exercise adherers.

Summary

   This paper has briefly outlined the background to exercise motivation, making specific reference to the problem of adherence/dropout. Some practical guidelines for starting and maintaining exercise are given. Strategies centred on both personal and environmental factors.

   The chapter has not addressed itself solely to teachers of physical education in schools since adherence to exercise is clearly a lifelong process. However, teachers would be wise to note these issues and adopt teaching strategies that encourage long-term involvement rather than short-term performance benefits. Just as we teach 'physical' concepts of exercise, such as the mechanics of muscle contraction, diet and exercise, exercise and the heart etc., so we should be starting to initiate teaching units on exercise motivation. These can be practical in nature where students are actively engaged in practical motivating strategies. Teachers can be active by operating exercise 'counselling'.

We can all get students exercising. However, we must consider ways of achieving regular exercise patterns, as outlined on the 'stairway to health-related fitness' in chapter 1. This requires us to consider the issues raised here.

References

ANDREW, G.M. et al. (1981). Reasons for dropout from exercise programmes in post-coronary patients. *Medicine and Science in Sports and Exercise*. Vol. 13(3).

BECKER, M.H. (1979). Understanding patient compliance: The contributions of attitudes and other psychological factors. In S.J. Cohen (ed). New directions in patient compliance. Lexington Books.

BIDDLE, S.J.H. (1984). Motivational issues in health-related fitness: A note of caution. *British Journal of Physical Education*, Vol. 15(1).

BIDDLE, S.J.H. (1986). Incentive schemes in exercise: Saints or sinners? *Health and Physical Education Project Newsletter*, No. 3.

BIDDLE, S.J.H. & ASHFORD, B. (1985). *Health beliefs, knowledge and attributions: A discriminant analysis of exercisers and non-exercisers*. Paper presented at British Association of Sports Sciences conference, West Sussex Institute of Higher Education, Chichester.

BRAWLEY, L.R. (1979). Motivating participation in the fitness group. *Recreation Research Review*, February.

BUFFONE, G.E. et al. (1984). Cognitive-behavioural strategies for promoting adherence to exercise. In M.L. Sachs & G.W. Buffone (Eds) *Running as therapy: An integrated approach*. University of Nebraska Press.

CARMODY, T.P. et al. (1980). Physical exercise rehabilitation: Long-term dropout rate in cardiac patients. *Journal of Behavioural Medicine*. Vol. 3(2).

DISHMAN, R.K. (1981a). Health psychology and exercise adherence. *Quest*, Vol. 33(2).

DISHMAN, R.K. (1981b). Biologic influences on exercise adherence. *Research Quarterly for Exercise and Sport*, Vol. 52.

DISHMAN, R.K. (1981c). Prediction of adherence to habitual physical activity. In F.J. Nagle & H.J. Montoye (Eds). *Exercise in health and disease*. C.C. Thomas.

DISHMAN, R.K. (1982). Compliance/adherence in health-related exercise. *Health Psychology*, Vol. 1(3).

DISHMAN, R.K. (1984). Motivation and exercise adherence. In J. Silva & R.S. Weinberg (Eds). *Psychological foundations of sport*. Human Kinetics.

DISHMAN, R.K. & GETTMAN, L.R. (1980). Psychobiologic influences on exercise adherence. *Journal of Sport Psychology*, Vol. 2.

DISHMAN, R.K., & ICKES, W. (1981). Self-motivation and adherence to therapeutic exercise. *Journal of Behavioural Medicine*.

DISHMAN, R.K., ICKES, W. & MORGAN, W.P. (1980). Self-motivation and adherence to habitual physical activity. *Journal of Applied Social Psychology*, Vol. 10(2).

EPSTEIN, L.H. et al. (1980). Attendance and fitness in aerobics exercise: The effects of contract and lottery procedures. *Behaviour Modification*, Vol. 4(4).

FOX, K.R., CORBIN, C.B. & COULDRY, W.H. (1985). Female physical estimation and attraction to physical activity. *Journal of Sport Psychology*, Vol. 7(2).

GILLIE, O. & RABY, S. (1984). *The Sunday Times ABC diet and body plan*. Hutchinson.

INGJER, F. & DAHL, H.A. (1979). Dropouts from an endurance training programme: Some histochemical and physiological aspects. *Scandinavian Journal of Sport Science*, Vol. 1(1).

KAU, M.L. & FISCHER, J. (1974). Self-modification of exercise behaviour. *Journal of Behaviour Therapy and Experimental Psychiatry*, Vol. 5.

LINDSAY-REID, E. & OSBORN, R.W. (1980). Readiness for exercise adoption. *Social Science and Medicine*, Vol. 14.

MAHONEY, M.J. & MAHONEY, K. (1976). *Permanent weight control*. W.W. Norton.

OLDRIDGE, N.B. (1982). Compliance and exercise in primary and secondary prevention of coronary heart disease: A review. *Preventative Medicine*, Vol. 11.

SLENKER, S.E. et al. (1984). Joggers versus non-exercisers: An analysis of knowledge, attitudes and beliefs about jogging. *Research Quarterly for Exercise and Sport*, Vol. 55.

SONSTROEM, R.J. (1978). Physical estimation and attraction scales: Research and rationale. *Medicine and Science in Sports*, Vol. 10.

WHITEHEAD, J.R. (1985). *The development of multidimensional scales for the measurement of locus of control of reinforcement for physical fitness behaviours*. Unpublished MSc thesis, Arizona State University.

This chapter first appeared in the *British Journal of Physical Education*, 1986, Vol. 17(1).

Chapter Eighteen

Competition and Health-Related Fitness

Andrew Sparkes

Competition is but one of many equally valuable experiences which should be made available to children within their physical education curriculum. However, the dependence of many physical education programmes upon the use of competition as both a 'motivator' and an end in itself is highly questionable, since this often results in children being 'turned off' physical education and developing negative attitudes to physical activity in general.

If it can be taken that one of the major aims of a Health-Related Fitness focus is to promote an active life-style and improve the quality of life, then the misuse and overuse of competition within such a programme may act to negate these aims.

Firstly, what evidence is there for the 'excess' of competition? If sport can be taken to be an institutionalised competitive activity, then the physical education curriculum in the majority of secondary schools is dominated by the process of competition, particularly in the form of invasion games and athletics (see Branford, 1985; Hill, 1985).

Many physical educators, due to their socialization within sport and the training institutions, accept the domination of the competitive experience as a 'taken for granted reality' (Schutz, 1962). When questioned about such dominance, the justifications given indicate the pervasiveness of certain assumptions concerning the nature of competitive sport and social life in general. These may be summarised as follows:

a) Competitive activities instil desirable personal qualities; it is 'character building'.
b) Competition is necessary to produce excellence.
c) Social life is highly competitive, therefore competitive sport prepares the individual to succeed in the 'outside world'.

Such assumptions have been strongly challenged elsewhere (Sparkes, 1985) in relation to their powerful influence on curriculum design which often produces a strong resistance to innovatory ideas, such as the introduction of Health-Related Fitness modules into the curriculum.

These assumptions contribute to a world view which is indicative of what Charles (1979) called a technocratic ideology, which has as its cornerstones the notion of mechanisticity (child as machine, with teachers and pupils a cog in a larger administrative machine), reproducability (production of uniform movement patterns for all children), componentiality (the development of isolated physical skills with a lack of concern for the whole person), and measurability (performance is evaluated in terms of precise quantifiable criteria in relation to pre-stated objectives). Based on the work of Berger, Berger and Kellner (1974), Bernstein (1971), and Esland (1971), Charles (1979) proposes that the dual forces of teacher training and previous schooling reinforce a recipe knowledge which is then recycled to children in the school situation.

"Their goal then becomes to produce the most efficient performer, their focus is on skills

teaching, their method reflects didactic uniformity, and their control medium is an elaborated language code." (Charles, 1979, p.282).

Such an approach is seen as detrimental in preparing students for a lifetime of meaningful physical activity.

If such a world view operates, then there is a need for individuals to clarify what they actually mean when they talk of competition, since Kildea (1982; 1983) has illustrated that even those who classify themselves as 'highly amongst those who classify themselves as 'highly confusion.

Many authors (Fielding, 1976; Nelson and Cody, 1975; Perry, 1975; Prvulovich, 1982), have discussed the nature of competition, however this paper will focus on the following conceptual areas:

A. competition.
B. a competitive attitude or orientation.
C. the pursuit of excellence.
D. the competitive context.

A.   COMPETITION

Competition may be taken to entail a struggle for *supremacy* between two or more sides. This clearly indicates that a social encounter is taking place between two or more individuals, in which there is a *conscious* struggle for a co-identified object which culminates in establishing the supremacy of one side. Linked to the use of supremacy is the notion of 'higher in rank', 'dominant' and 'highest in achievement', which leads individuals to view rewards in activities as being mutually exclusive and to evaluate achievement in strictly relativistic terms, in which success is dependent upon the failure of others. The notion of struggle involves 'to make great efforts or attempts' to 'strive or labour', to make way with difficulty (awareness of opposing force).

B.   A COMPETITIVE ATTITUDE OR ORIENTATION

A competitive attitude/orientation is a condition in which an individual directs effort towards surpassing the performance of another or others. This orientation is necessary for competition but it can also be an independent attitude held by an individual in a non-social setting. Therefore competition is *not* occurring because others are not necessarily aware of the efforts to surpass, hence there is no 'other' side or 'struggle'.

C.   THE PURSUIT OF EXCELLENCE

The pursuit of excellence is a condition in which an individual's effort is directed towards the attainment of a personal standard or goal without any particular reference to the performance of others, and is intimately linked to the notion of *self-improvement* in meeting a challenge, e.g. to complete a marathon, to climb a mountain, to swim continuously for one hour. There is still a form of struggle, but the struggle is *personal* i.e. there is no other side.

Such a pursuit fosters a 'parallel action orientation' which is characterised by a tendency to see rewards in a situation as being independent of the behaviour of any other participants. Goal achievement then depends on how their own behaviour measures up to standards based on *personal* rather than relativistic criteria; i.e. the standards they use to evaluate themselves emerge out of expectations based on past personal experiences rather than out of any direct comparison with others.

It needs to be stated strongly that competition and the pursuit of excellence are distinctly different behaviours and should not be confused. Excellence can occur in competition but the two are not synonymous. As early as 1957 Combs noted:
"Competition is not concerned with the production of quality, but with winning acceptance ... the aim of competition often becomes one of winning the market rather than producing a better product. The salesman competing for my business is not so much interested in producing a good product as in *selling* his product regardless of its defects. He does not display its weaknesses, he hides them. Competition seeks to prove superiority, even if it does not exist". (Combs, 1957, p.265).

Whilst Whol (1970) is critical of the unnecessary and harmful overspecialisation which competition produces since it is contrary to the principles of all-round development and improvement of the state of health.

D.   THE COMPETITIVE CONTEXT

Finally, the competitive context is one which provides a social structure and set of rules. These rules are essentially primary, constitutive rules in which one of the components is that they define the manner in which winning is to be achieved by the participants. Since such rules are essential to sports in that they define the activity, then it can be taken that these provide a competitive context.

Individuals do not, however, enter a competitive context with identical motivations. The reasons for participation vary over time for any individual involved in any activity. The game or activity, therefore, provides a structure in which participants can gain particular kinds of experience, and whilst the rules determine the manner of winning and losing they do *not* determine the motivations that participants

bring with them into the competitive context, nor the experiences that they seek.

Having outlined such conceptual categories one is in a more enlightened position to consider just which of these is more appropriate as the central focus of a Health-Related Fitness programme. Evidence of chidren's participation needs may also assist in making an informed decision and overcome the misguided notion that children take part in competitive games and activities within physical education because they *enjoy* competition (see Sparkes and Dickenson, 1985).

The notion of incentive motivation as proposed by Alderman (1978) and Alderman and Wood (1976), is relevant at this point. Their studies consider what it is about an activity itself, in terms of its nature and demands, that motivates a child to persist in his/her participation over time.

Incentive motivation refers to the incentive value an individual attaches to the outcomes or experiences he/she perceives as being available within a particular activity. This is highly important since each individual is constantly faced with alternatives, such as going for a swim or watching T.V., playing football or repairing the motorcycle. The choice of action that the individual selects, and persists with, comes about in part because of the kinds of incentives that they find particularly attractive at that moment, and the value attached to them.

Using a sample of 425 11 to 14 year old male Canadian ice hockey players, seven major incentive systems were identified by Alderman and Wood (1976) as follows: power, independence, affiliation, stress, excellence, aggression and success. With these children a consistent pattern emerged for their participation, in which the two strongest and most consistent incentive conditions for young athletes were those of affiliation and excellence, with stress incentives a consistent third. These

results were considered by Alderman (1978) in combination with the findings obtained from several thousand athletes from different sports (ages 11 to 18 years). A similar pattern of priorities emerged leading him to conclude that children are basically motivated by the same system *regardless* of their age, sex and culture.

Likewise, Passer (1982), in reviewing recent research into children's participation motives in a large number of different sports, suggests that children's and adolescents' participation motives may be grouped into the following six major categories: affiliation, skill development, excitement, success and status, fitness, and energy release.

These categories are similar to those proposed by Alderman and Wood (1976) in which affiliation relates to incentives associated with opportunities for social intercourse, or being socially reassured that one is acceptable and worthwhile by the making of new friends or the maintenance of already existing friendships. Excellence (skill development) is concerned with incentives revolving around opportunities to improve skills or learn new ones, to do something very well for its own sake or to do it better than anyone else *regardless* of whether one wins or not. Stress (excitement) involves incentives associated with opportunities for

excitement, tension, pressure and the pure action that sport can provide. In terms of a focus on Health-Related Fitness, a significant inclusion in Passer's (1982) scheme is the category of fitness.

It needs to be recognised that there are difficulties in attempting to rank these factors in terms of their perceived importance, since individual differences exist, hence the reasons that are important to some children will not necessarily be the reasons that are paramount to others. However, as Passer (1982) points out: "The most general conclusion is that with the exception of energy release, all of these motives are viewed by most children as important determinants of their sports involvement". (Passer, 1982, p.232).

It would appear, therefore, that a great many children do not participate, even in competitive activities in order to 'beat others', 'dominate others', or to 'emphasise superiority'. They are attracted by the opportunities to meet personal needs which are offered within a competitive context. An undue emphasis on the competitive element, i.e. the 'winning' and 'beating of others' in any activity may reduce the opportunity to satisfy such needs as affiliation, excellence and stress.

The findings of Alderman (1978), Alderman and Wood (1976), and Passer (1982) are based on studies involving North American children. Despite Alderman's (1978) view that children are basically motivated by the same incentives regardless of their age, sport, sex and culture, attempts to generalize such findings to British children are problematic since in any country, sport, and the meanings attached to it by the participants, is located within its own specific socio-cultural framework and needs to be analysed in relation to this. However, recent British studies by Dickenson (1985), who investigated children's (aged 11 to 14 years) activity patterns, and Crowder (1985), who was concerned with adolescent girls who 'dropped out' of physical education, indicate that there may be important similarities between North American and British children. Both British studies reinforce the view that children interpret their involvement in competitive sport differently than their adult teachers. They do indeed seek to satisfy such needs as affiliation and excellence, whilst 'intense competition' is perceived as a major reason for 'turning off'.

In relation to the above, the work of Luschen (1969) is of significance. He compared the spontaneously formed play group with the organised competitive team in terms of the level of formal organisation inherent in each. The level of formal organisation was seen to have implications not only for the action of group members, but also for their relationships with one another, and the nature of their experiences which for the participants in each group were *qualitatively* different. Hence, as the level of formal organisation increases along with the emphasis on the 'winning' and 'beating of others', the kinds of experience available to children within that structure changes significantly. Attempts need to be made therefore, to identify participation motives since this would provide valuable information concerning the opportunities and outcomes that children seek from sport. Such knowledge would be of great importance to physical educators who are interested in structuring the sports environment to reflect the child's incentive motives and thereby provide a maximally rewarding expereience.

The warning for those would place an undue emphasis on the competitive element within a Health-Related Fitness programme is clear. If children are continuously placed in a competitive context in which their incentive needs cannot be met, then their enthusiasm and interest is likely to wane rapidly. The end result for many will be to cease participation in any sort of physical activity once they are free from compulsory education in schools, and surely

this is the exact opposite of what any teacher concerned with Health-Related Fitness hopes for.

Careful consideration should be given by teachers to the implications of using competition in a Health-Related Fitness programme and equally valuable alternatives should not be overlooked, e.g. the pursuit of excellence which would appear a more appropriate focus in promoting an active lifestyle. Competition has its place but as Leonard (1973) has pointed out, in the proper proportion competition is like a little salt:

". . . it adds to the zest of the game of life itself, but when the seasoning is mistaken for the substance, only sickness can follow." (Leonard, 1973, pp 45-46).

References
ALDERMAN, R.B. (1978). Strategies for motivating young athletes. In W. Straub (Ed). *Sports psychology: an analysis of athlete behaviour.* New York: Movement Publications.
ALDERMAN, R.B. & WOOD, N.L. (1976). An analysis of incentive motivation in young Canadian athletes. *Canadian Journal of Applied Sport Sciences,* I.
BERGER, P., BERGER, B. & KELLNER, M. (1974). *The homeless mind.* New York: Vintage Books.
BERNSTEIN, B. (1971). *Class, codes and control,* London: Routledge & Kegan Paul.
BRANFORD, C. (1985). *The physical education curriculum for boys in a local education authority.* Unpublished M.Phil. Thesis, University of Technology, Loughborough.
CHARLES, J.M. (1979). Technocratic ideology in physical education. *Quest.*

COMBS, A. (1957). The myth of competition. *Child Education*.

CROWDER, G. (1985). *Avoidance behaviour of adolescent girls in physical education*. Unpublished B.Sc. Thesis, University of Technology, Loughborough.

DICKENSON, B. (1985). *Attitude and perceptions of young children towards physical education*. Unpublished M.Phil. Thesis, University of Technology, Loughborough.

ESLAND, G. (1971). Teaching and learning as the organisation of knowledge. In M.F.D. Young (Ed), *Knowledge and control*. London: Collier MacMillan.

FIELDING, M. (1976). Against competition. *Proceedings of philosophy of education society of Great Britain*.

HILL, C. (1985). *An analysis of the physical education curriculum in a local education authority*. Unpublished M.Phil. Thesis, University of Technology, Loughborough.

KILDEA, A.E. (1982). Competition: a model for conception. In C. Thomas (Chair) *Proceedings of the philosophic society for the study of sport*. New York, Buffalo Press.

KILDEA, A.E. (1983). Competition: a model for conception. *Quest*.

LEONARD, G.B. (1973). Winning isn't everything, it's nothing. *Intelligence Digest*.

LUSCHEN, G.B. (1969). Small group research and the group in sport. In KENYON, G. (Ed), *Sociology of sport*, North Palm Beach, Fla: The Athletic Institute.

NELSON, K. & CODY, C. (1979). Competition, co−operation and fair play. *International review of sport sociology*.

PASSER, M.W. (1982). Children in sport: participation motives and psychological stress. *Quest*.

PERRY, L.R. (1975). Competition and co-operation. *British Journal of Educational Studies*.

PRVULOVICH, Z.R. (1982). In defence of competition. *Journal of Philosophy of Education*.

SCHUTZ, A. (1962). *The problem of social reality – collected papers I*. The Hague: Martinus Nijhoff.

SPARKES, A.C. (1985). The competitive mansion – build on sand. *British Journal of Physical Education*.

SPARKES, A.C. & DICKENSON B., (1985). Participation in competition – a case of mistaken identity. *Scottish Journal of Physical Education*.

WHOL, A. (1970). Competitive sport and its social functions. *International Review of Sports Sociology*.